Core Knowledge Language Arts®

Domain 1
Nursery Rhymes and Fables

Domain 2
The Five Senses

Domain 3
Stories

Domain 4
Plants

Domain 5
Farms

Domain 6
Native Americans

Domains 1 - 6
Tell it Again!™ Workbook

Listening & Learning™ Strand
KINDERGARTEN

Amplify learning.

Core Knowledge®

Core Knowledge Language Arts®

Domain 1: Nursery Rhymes and Fables
Tell it Again!™ Workbook

Listening & Learning™ Strand
KINDERGARTEN

Amplify learning.

Core Knowledge®

Dear Family Member,

Your child will be enjoying some popular nursery rhymes at school over the next several days. Listening to nursery rhymes and then saying them will help your child develop an awareness of language that will enable him/her to become a better reader and writer. Your child will listen to and discuss many nursery rhymes, including:

- "Rain, Rain, Go Away"
- "It's Raining, It's Pouring"
- "Jack Be Nimble"
- "Little Jack Horner"
- "Jack and Jill"
- "Little Miss Muffet"
- "This Little Pig Went to Market"
- "One, Two, Buckle My Shoe"

I have included a copy of all of the nursery rhymes your child will hear. Below are some suggestions for activities that you may do at home to continue enjoying the nursery rhymes and to help your child remember them.

1. Reciting Nursery Rhymes

Say or sing the nursery rhyme with your child or take turns saying the lines of the rhyme. Think of ways to act out the rhyme or use gestures while saying it.

2. Nursery Rhyme Characters and Events

Talk with your child about the characters and events in the nursery rhymes. Ask questions using the vocabulary of the rhyme such as, "What frightened Miss Muffet?" Also, make personal connections to the rhymes with questions such as, "Do you remember the time that we wanted the rain to go away so we could go to the park?"

3. Illustrating Nursery Rhymes

Have your child draw or paint a picture of one of the nursery rhymes and then tell you about it. Again, ask questions to keep your child talking about the nursery rhyme.

4. Rhyming Words in Nursery Rhymes

Many nursery rhymes have rhyming words. Say a line or two from the nursery rhymes your child has learned about, and ask your child to identify the rhyming words. Next, say the rhyme but leave out the second rhyming word for your child to say. Finally, ask your child if s/he can think of other words that rhyme with the ones identified in the nursery rhyme.

5. Read Aloud Each Day

It is very important that you read to your child every day. I have attached a list of recommended trade books featuring nursery rhymes that may be found at the library. You may also want to look for nonfiction books to share about topics—such as spiders or stars—mentioned in the nursery rhymes to share with your child.

6. Sayings and Phrases: It's Raining Cats and Dogs

Your child will also learn the well-known saying, "it's raining cats and dogs." The next time there is a downpour, will you or your child be the first one to say, "It's raining cats and dogs"?

Be sure to let your child know how much you enjoy hearing what s/he has learned at school.

Recommended Resources for Nursery Rhymes and Fables

Trade Books

Nursery Rhymes

1. *Arroz con leche: Popular Songs and Rhymes from Latin America,* selected and illustrated by Lulu Delacre (Scholastic, 1992) ISBN 978-0590418867

2. *Diez Deditos: Ten Little Fingers and Other Play Rhymes and Action Songs from Latin America,* selected, arranged, and translated by José-Luis Orozco (Penguin Group, 2002) ISBN 978-0142300879

3. *De Colores and Other Latin-American Folk Songs for Children,* selected, arranged, and translated by José-Luis Orozco (Penguin Group, 1999) ISBN 978-0140565485

4. *Favorite Nursery Rhymes from Mother Goose,* illustrated by Scott Gustafson (The Greenwich Workshop Press, 2007) ISBN 978-0867130973

5. *Hush: A Thai Lullaby,* by Minfong Ho (Scholastic, 2000) ISBN 978-0531071663

6. *Mother Goose: A Collection of Classic Nursery Rhymes,* by Michael Hague (Henry Holt, 1988) ISBN 978-0805002140

7. *Mother Goose Remembers,* by Clare Beaton (Barefoot Books, 2006) ISBN 978-1846860034

8. *Pocketful of Posies: A Treasury of Nursery Rhymes,* by Salley Mavor (Houghton Mifflin Harcourt, 2010) ISBN 978-0618737406

9. *Read-Aloud Rhymes for the Very Young,* by Jack Prelutsky and illustrated by Marc Brown (Knopf Books for Young Readers, 1986) ISBN 978-0394872186

10. *The Real Mother Goose,* illustrated by Blanche Fisher Wright (Scholastic, 1994) ISBN 978-0590225175

11. *Three Little Kittens,* by Paul Galdone (Clarion, 1988) ISBN 978-0899197968

Fables

12. *Aesop's Fables,* by Jerry Pinkney (Chronicle Books, 2000) ISBN 978-1587170003

13. *Aesop's Fables,* by Beverly Naidoo and illustrated by Piet Grobler (Frances Lincoln Children's Books, 2011) ISBN 978-1847800077

14. *The Ant and the Grasshopper,* by Rebecca Emberley and illustrated by Ed Emberley (Roaring Book Press, 2012) ISBN 978-1596434936

15. *How the Leopard Got His Claws,* by Chinua Achebe and illustrated by Mary GrandPré (Candlewick, 2011) 978-0763648053

16. *The Lion and the Mouse,* retold and illustrated by Bernadette Watts (North-South Books, 2007) ISBN 978-0735821293

17. *Little Cloud and Lady Wind,* by Toni Morrison and Slade Morrison and illustrated by Sean Qualls (Simon & Schuster, 2010) ISBN 978-1416985235

18. *The Tortoise and the Hare,* adapted and illustrated by Janet Stevens (Holiday House, 1985) ISBN 978-0823405640

19. *Town Mouse, Country Mouse,* by Jan Brett (Putnam Juvenile, 2003) ISBN 978-0698119864

20. *The Wise Fool: Fables from the Islamic World,* by Shahrukh Husain and Micha Archer (Barefoot Books, 2011) ISBN 978-1846862267

Websites and Other Resources

Student Resources

1. Rhyming Game
   http://bit.ly/XkQm8C

Family Resources

2. Mother Goose
   http://bit.ly/ZsvgEM

3. Morals from Fables
   http://bit.ly/XkQLb2

4. Aesop's Fables
   http://aesopfables.com

5. Learning to Read
   http://1.usa.gov/VPTTdJ

Roses Are Red

Roses are red,

Violets are blue,

Sugar is sweet,

And so are you.

Ring Around the Rosie

Ring around the rosie,

A pocket full of posies;

Ashes, ashes,

We all fall down.

Rain, Rain, Go Away

Rain, rain, go away,

Come again some other day.

Little Johnny wants to play,

Rain, rain, go away.

Jack Be Nimble

Jack be nimble,

Jack be quick,

Jack jump over

The candlestick.

Little Jack Horner

Little Jack Horner

Sat in a corner,

Eating his Christmas pie;

He put in his thumb,

And pulled out a plum,

And said, "What a good boy am I!"

Jack and Jill

Jack and Jill went up the hill

To fetch a pail of water;

Jack fell down and broke his crown,

And Jill came tumbling after.

Little Miss Muffet

Little Miss Muffet

Sat on a tuffet,

Eating her curds and whey;

Along came a spider,

Who sat down beside her

And frightened Miss Muffet away.

This Little Pig Went to Market

This little pig went to market,

This little pig stayed home;

This little pig had roast beef,

This little pig had none,

And this little pig cried,
"Wee-wee-wee,"

all the way home.

One, Two, Buckle My Shoe

One, two,

Buckle my shoe;

Three, four,

Shut the door;

Five, six,

Pick up sticks;

Seven, eight,

Lay them straight;

Nine, ten,

A big fat hen.

Star Light, Star Bright

Star light, star bright,

First star I see tonight,

I wish I may, I wish I might,

Have the wish I wish tonight.

Twinkle, Twinkle, Little Star

by Jane Taylor

Twinkle, twinkle, little star,

How I wonder what you are.

Up above the world so high,

Like a diamond in the sky.

Twinkle, twinkle, little star,

How I wonder what you are!

Hickory, Dickory, Dock

Hickory, dickory, dock,

The mouse ran up the clock.

The clock struck one,

The mouse ran down,

Hickory, dickory, dock.

Diddle, Diddle, Dumpling

Diddle, diddle, dumpling, my son John,

Went to bed with his stockings on;

One shoe off, and one shoe on,

Diddle, diddle, dumpling, my son John.

Little Bo Peep

Little Bo Peep has lost her sheep,

And can't tell where to find them;

Leave them alone, and they'll come home,

Wagging their tails behind them.

Little Boy Blue

Little Boy Blue,

Come blow your horn,

The sheep's in the meadow,

The cow's in the corn;

But where is the boy

Who looks after the sheep?

He's under a haystack,

Fast asleep.

Baa, Baa, Black Sheep

Baa, baa, black sheep,

Have you any wool?

Yes, sir, yes, sir,

Three bags full.

One for the master,

And one for the dame,

And one for the little boy

Who lives down the lane.

Humpty Dumpty

Humpty Dumpty

sat on a wall,

Humpty Dumpty had

a great fall.

All the king's horses,

And all the king's men,

Couldn't put Humpty

together again.

⑩ Recording Sheet for Recitation of Nursery Rhymes Assessment

Note: You will want to find a time for each student to choose one or more nursery rhymes to recite for you or the class. Use this recording sheet to document this assessment.

Student's Name _____

Date _____

Title of Nursery Rhyme _____

Scoring: _____

10 Recited entire nursery rhyme correctly

5 Recited some lines of the nursery rhyme correctly

1 Was not able to recite any lines of the nursery rhyme correctly

Comments _____

_____

_____

_____

Dear Family Member,

I hope that you and your child have been having fun with nursery rhymes at home. At school, your child has become familiar with these additional rhymes:

- "Star Light, Star Bright"
- "Twinkle, Twinkle, Little Star"
- "Hickory, Dickory, Dock"
- "Diddle, Diddle, Dumpling"
- "Little Bo Peep"
- "Little Boy Blue"
- "Baa, Baa, Black Sheep"
- "Humpty Dumpty"

Continue to use the activities that were suggested in the previous parent letter for talking about, illustrating, and reciting the nursery rhymes.

Today, your child listened to the well-known fable "The Lion and the Mouse," and learned that fables are short stories that teach a lesson, which is called the moral of the story. The students will also become familiar with the fables "The Dog and His Reflection" and "The Hare and the Tortoise," and will learn that many fables have animal characters that act like people.

Below are some suggestions for activities that you may do at home to continue enjoying the fables heard at school.

1. Characters and Events in Fables

Talk with your child about the characters and events in the fables. Make personal connections to the fables with questions such as, "Has a little friend ever been a great friend to you?"

2. Illustrating Fables

Have your child draw or paint a picture of one of the fables and then tell you about it. Again, ask questions to keep your child talking about the fable. Another option is to create a three-part picture that shows the beginning, middle, and end of the fable.

3. Different Versions of Fables

Tell or read to your child different versions of a fable. Talk about ways the different versions are the same and how they are different.

4. Words to Use

Below is a list of some of the words your child will be using and learning about. Try to use these words as they come up in everyday speech with your child.

- *wish*—I like to wish upon a star when it is nighttime.
- *wagging*—Our dogs are wagging their tails because they are happy to see us.
- *wool*—My wool blanket keeps me warm.
- *reflection*—I can see my reflection in the mirror.

5. Read Aloud Each Day

It is very important that you read to your child every day. Refer to the list of recommended trade books sent home earlier in this domain for fables and collections of fables to share with your child. Be sure to talk about the moral of each fable, and how the moral might apply to you and your child.

Remember to let your child know how much you enjoy hearing what s/he has learned at school.

Name _____

Directions: These three pictures show events from "The Dog and His Reflection." Cut out the three pictures. Think about what is happening in each one. Put the pictures in order to show the beginning, middle, and end of the fable. Glue them in the correct order on a piece of paper.

Name _____

Directions: I am going to say a sentence using a word you have heard in this domain. First I will say the word and then use it in a sentence. If I use the word correctly in my sentence, circle the smiling face. If I do not use the word correctly in my sentence, circle the frowning face. I will say each sentence two times. Let's do number one together.

1. ☺ ☹

2. ☺ ☹

3. ☺ ☹

4. ☺ ☹

5. ☺ ☹

6. ☺ ☹

7. ☺ ☹

8. ☺ ☹

9. ☺ ☹

10. ☺ ☹

Name _____

Directions: Circle the picture that answers the question about the nursery rhyme or fable.

1.			
2.			
3.			
4.			
5.			
6.			

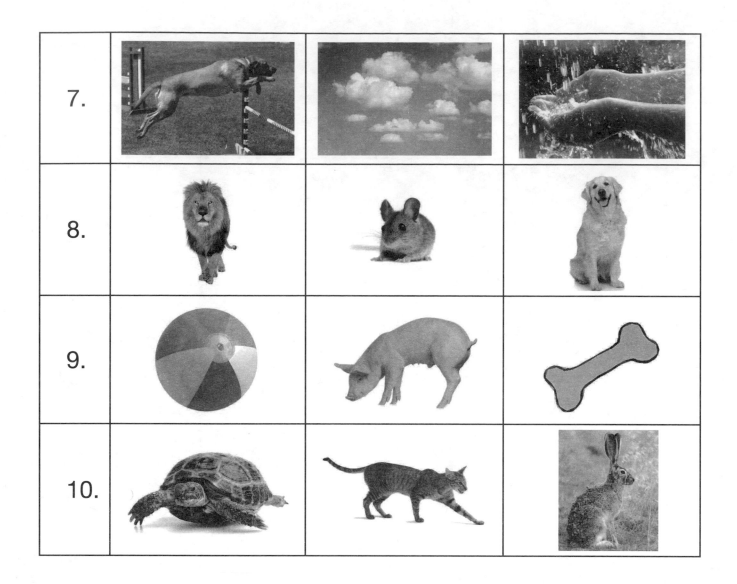

Name _____

Directions: Listen to the two words that your teacher says. If the two words rhyme, circle the smiling face. If the two words do not rhyme, circle the frowning face.

1. 🙂   🙁

2. 🙂   🙁

3. 🙂   🙁

4. 🙂   🙁

5. 🙂   🙁

6. 🙂   🙁

7. 🙂   🙁

8. 🙂   🙁

CORE KNOWLEDGE LANGUAGE ARTS

SERIES EDITOR-IN-CHIEF
E. D. Hirsch, Jr.

PRESIDENT
Linda Bevilacqua

EDITORIAL STAFF

Carolyn Gosse, Senior Editor - Preschool
Khara Turnbull, Materials Development Manager
Michelle L. Warner, Senior Editor - Listening & Learning

Mick Anderson
Robin Blackshire
Maggie Buchanan
Paula Coyner
Sue Fulton
Sara Hunt
Erin Kist
Robin Luecke
Rosie McCormick
Cynthia Peng
Liz Pettit
Ellen Sadler
Deborah Samley
Diane Auger Smith
Sarah Zelinke

DESIGN AND GRAPHICS STAFF

Scott Ritchie, Creative Director

Kim Berrall
Michael Donegan
Liza Greene
Matt Leech
Bridget Moriarty
Lauren Pack

CONSULTING PROJECT MANAGEMENT SERVICES

ScribeConcepts.com

ADDITIONAL CONSULTING SERVICES

Ang Blanchette
Dorrit Green
Carolyn Pinkerton

ACKNOWLEDGMENTS

These materials are the result of the work, advice, and encouragement of numerous individuals over many years. Some of those singled out here already know the depth of our gratitude; others may be surprised to find themselves thanked publicly for help they gave quietly and generously for the sake of the enterprise alone. To helpers named and unnamed we are deeply grateful.

CONTRIBUTORS TO EARLIER VERSIONS OF THESE MATERIALS

Susan B. Albaugh, Kazuko Ashizawa, Nancy Braier, Kathryn M. Cummings, Michelle De Groot, Diana Espinal, Mary E. Forbes, Michael L. Ford, Ted Hirsch, Danielle Knecht, James K. Lee, Diane Henry Leipzig, Martha G. Mack, Liana Mahoney, Isabel McLean, Steve Morrison, Juliane K. Munson, Elizabeth B. Rasmussen, Laura Tortorelli, Rachael L. Shaw, Sivan B. Sherman, Miriam E. Vidaver, Catherine S. Whittington, Jeannette A. Williams

We would like to extend special recognition to Program Directors Matthew Davis and Souzanne Wright who were instrumental to the early development of this program.

SCHOOLS

We are truly grateful to the teachers, students, and administrators of the following schools for their willingness to field test these materials and for their invaluable advice: Capitol View Elementary, Challenge Foundation Academy (IN), Community Academy Public Charter School, Lake Lure Classical Academy, Lepanto Elementary School, New Holland Core Knowledge Academy, Paramount School of Excellence, Pioneer Challenge Foundation Academy, New York City PS 26R (The Carteret School), PS 30X (Wilton School), PS 50X (Clara Barton School), PS 96Q, PS 102X (Joseph O. Loretan), PS 104Q (The Bays Water), PS 214K (Michael Friedsam), PS 223Q (Lyndon B. Johnson School), PS 308K (Clara Cardwell), PS 333Q (Goldie Maple Academy), Sequoyah Elementary School, South Shore Charter Public School, Spartanburg Charter School, Steed Elementary School, Thomas Jefferson Classical Academy, Three Oaks Elementary, West Manor Elementary.

And a special thanks to the CKLA Pilot Coordinators Anita Henderson, Yasmin Lugo-Hernandez, and Susan Smith, whose suggestions and day-to-day support to teachers using these materials in their classrooms was critical.

Amplify learning.

Domain 2: The Five Senses
Tell It Again!™ Workbook

Listening & Learning™ Strand
KINDERGARTEN

Core Knowledge®

Name _____

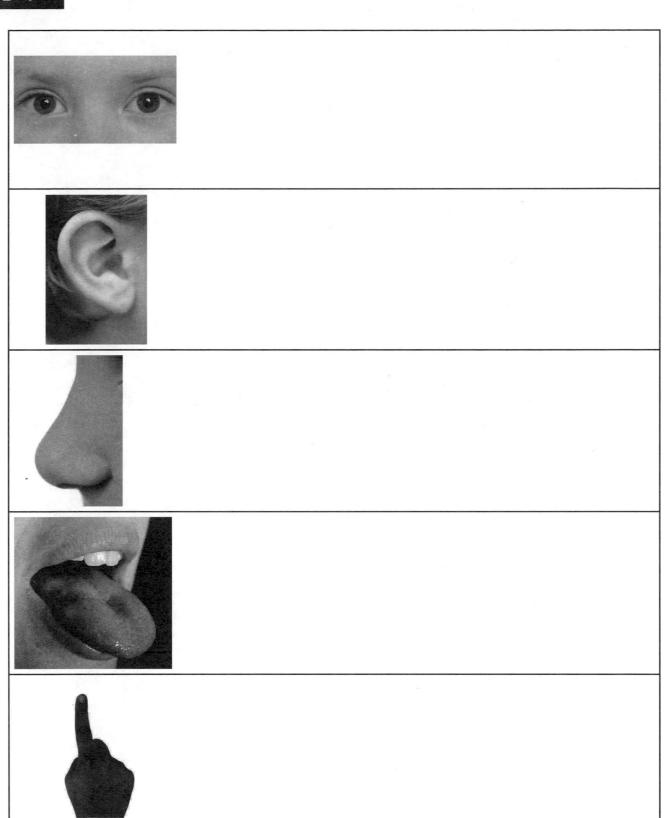

Directions: Draw what you discovered on your walk next to the sense(s) that helped you discover it.

Dear Family Member,

Over the next several days, your child will be learning about the five senses. Over the course of the domain, your child will learn about each of the five senses and the respective body parts.

Below are some suggestions for activities that you can do at home to continue learning about the five senses.

1. "My Senses Are Amazing" Poem

Read the following poem to your child. Point to each body part as you read.

My Senses Are Amazing

My senses are amazing,

They help me do so much.

My eyes can see, my ears can hear,

My skin and hands can touch.

My senses are amazing,

They make me happy, too.

My tongue can taste the food I eat,

My nose can smell perfume.

My senses are amazing,

They keep me safe from harm.

My nose smells smoke, my skin feels heat,

My ears hear fire alarms.

My senses are amazing,

And now you know them well.

Let's say all five together now:

Sight, hearing, taste, touch, smell.

2. Sensory Walk

Take a walk with your child, and encourage him/her to talk about what s/he sees, hears, smells, etc. Have your child identify which body part is associated with each sense.

3. Texture Hunt

Your child will learn that objects have many different types of textures. Walk around the house or outside with your child and touch a variety of objects. Talk with your child about the texture of each of the objects. Use the word *texture* as often as possible.

4. Words to Use

Below is a list of some of the words that your child will be using at school. Try to use these words as they come up in everyday speech with your child.

- *harm*—Don't get too close to the fire; it could harm you.
- *protect*—Our umbrella protects us from the rain and keeps us dry.
- *invisible*—The wind is invisible.
- *scents*—What kind of scents do you smell in you neighborhood?

5. Sayings and Phrases: Look Before You Leap

Your child will learn the well-known sayings "look before you leap" and "better safe than sorry." You may want to use these sayings the next time you and/or your child think ahead before acting.

6. Read Aloud Each Day

It is very important that you read to your child each day. The local library has many books on the five senses and a list of books and other resources relevant to this topic is attached to this letter.

Be sure to praise your child whenever s/he shares what has been learned at school.

Recommended Resources for The Five Senses

Trade Book List

1. *Bee-bim Bop!* by Linda Sue Park (Sandpiper, Houghton Mifflin Harcourt, 2005) ISBN 978-0547076713

2. *Brian's Bird,* by Patricia Anne Davis (Whitman, 2000) ISBN 978-0807508817

3. *A Button in Her Ear,* by Ada B. Litchfield (Albert Whitman & Company, 1976) ISBN 978-0807509876

4. *Eating Well,* by Liz Gogerly (Crabtree Publishing Company, 2009) ISBN 978-0778741176

5. *Eyes (Human Body),* by Robert James (Rourke Publishing, 1995) ISBN 978-1571031044

6. *First Delights: A Book About the Five Senses,* by Tasha Tudor (Price, Stern, Sloan, 1988) ISBN 978-0448093277

7. *The Five Senses (It's Science),* by Sally Hewitt (Scholastic, 2002) ISBN 978-051623823

8. *The Five Senses: Hearing,* by Maria Ruis (Barron's Educational Series, Inc., 1985) ISBN 978-0812035636

9. *The Five Senses: Sight,* by Maria Rius (Barron's Educational Series, Inc., 1985) ISBN 978-0812035643

10. *The Five Senses: Smell,* by Maria Rius (Barron's Educational Series, Inc., 1985) ISBN 978-0812035650

11. *The Five Senses: Taste,* by Maria Rius (Barron's Educational Series, Inc., 1985) ISBN 978-0812035667

12. *The Five Senses: Touch,* by Maria Rius (Barron's Educational Series, Inc., 1985) ISBN 978-0812035674

13. *Fuel the Body: Eating Well,* by Amanda Doering Tourville (Picture Window Books, 2008) ISBN 978-1404848146

14. *Get Up and Go!,* by Nancy Carlson (Penguin Group, 2008) ISBN 978-0142410646

15. *Go Wash Up: Keeping Clean,* by Amanda Doering Tourville (Coughlan Publishing, 2008) ISBN 978-1404848085

16. *Green Start: The Five Senses,* by Ikids (Innovative Kids, 2009) ISBN 978-1584768128

17. *Hanni and Beth: Safe and Sound,* (Blue Marlin, 2007) 978-0979291807

18. *Happy Birthday Moon,* by Frank Asch (Aladdin, 2000) ISBN 978-0689835445

19. *Hearing,* by Katie Dicker (M. Evans and Company, 2009) ISBN 978-0237536008

20. *Hearing (I Know That!),* by Claire Llewellyn (Franklin Watts, 2009) ISBN 978-0749688950

21. *Hearing Things,* by Allan Fowler (Childrens Press, Inc., 1991) ISBN 978-0516449098

22. *The Hickory Chair,* by Lisa Rowe Fraustino (Arthur Levine Books, 2001) ISBN 978-0590522489

23. *It Looked Like Spilt Milk,* by Charles Shaw (HarperFestival, 1992) ISBN 978-0064433129

24. *Kami and the Yaks,* by Andrea Stenn Stryer (Bay Otter Press, 2007) ISBN 978-0977896103

25. *The Listening Walk,* by Paul Showers and Aliki (HarperCollins, 1993) ISBN 978-0064433228

26. *Look! A Book About Sight,* by Dana Meachen Rau (Picture Window Books, 2005) ISBN 978-1404810198

27. *Look, Listen, Taste, Touch, and Smell: Learning About Your Five Senses,* by Hill Nettleton (Picture Window Books, 2006) ISBN 978-1404805088

28. *Looking Out for Sarah,* by Glenna Lang (Charles Bridge, 2001) ISBN 978-1570916076

29. *Mandy Sue Day,* by Roberta Karim (Clarion, 1994) ISBN 978-0618316755

30. *Mice Squeak, We Speak,* by Arnold L. Shapiro and illustrated by Tomie dePaola (Puffin, 2000) ISBN 978-0698118737

31. *Moses Goes to a Concert,* by Isaac Millman (Farrar Straus, 1998) ISBN 978-0374453664

32. *My Amazing Body: A First Look at Health and Fitness,* by Pat Thomas (Barron's Educational Series, Inc., 2001) ISBN 978-0764121197

33. *My Five Senses,* by Aliki (HarperFestival, 1991) ISBN 978-0440843542

34. *My Senses Help Me,* by Bobbie Kalman (Crabtree Publishing Company, 2010) ISBN 978-0778794721

35. *No One Saw: Ordinary Things Through the Eyes of an Artist,* by Bob Raczka (Millbook Press, 2001) ISBN 978-0761316480

36. *Oh, the Things You Can Do that Are Good for You!: All About Staying Healthy,* by Tish Rabe (Random House, Inc., 2001) ISBN 978-0375810985

37. *Polar Bear, Polar Bear,* by Bill Martin Jr. (Henry Holt and Co., 2010) ISBN 978-0805092455

38. *Rainbow Joe and Me,* by Maria Diaz Strom (Lee and Low Books, 1999) ISBN 978-1584300502

39. *Screaming Kind of Day,* by Rachna Gilmore (Fitzhenry & Whiteside, 1999) ISBN 978-1550416619

40. *Seeing,* by Katie Dicker (M. Evans and Company, 2011) ISBN 978-0237544485

41. *Seven Blind Mice,* by Ed Young (Puffin Books, 2002) ISBN 978-0698118959

42. *Shhhh . . . A Book About Hearing,* by Dana Meachen Rau (Picture Window Books, 2005) ISBN 978-1404810181

43. *Sight,* by Annalise Bekkering (Weigl Publishers, Inc., 2009) ISBN 978-1605960531

44. *Sign Language,* by Lora Heller (Sterling Children's Books, 2012) ISBN 978-1402763922

45. *Sleep Is for Everyone (Let's-Read-and-Find-out Science Book),* by Paul Showers (HarperCollins Publishers, 1997) ISBN 978-0064451413

46. *Smelling and Tasting (I Know That!),* by Claire Llewellyn (Orchard/Watts Group, 2004) ISBN 978-0749657260

47. *Tasting and Smelling,* by Katie Dicker (M. Evans and Company, 2011) ISBN 978-0237544492

48. *Touching (I Know That!),* by Claire Llewellyn (Franklin Watts, 2009) ISBN 978-0749688974

49. *Touching and Feeling,* by Katie Dicker (M. Evans and Company, 2011) ISBN 978-0237544508

50. *What is Taste?,* by Jennifer Boothroyd (Lerner Classroom, 2009) ISBN 978-0761350170

51. *You Can't Smell a Flower with Your Ear! All About Your 5 Senses,* by Joanna Cole (Penguin Young Readers, 1994) ISBN 978-0448404691

52. *You Can't Taste a Pickle with Your Ear: A Book About Your 5 Senses,* by Harriet Ziefert and illustrated by Amanda Haley (Blue Apple, 2002) ISBN 978-1929766680

53. *Your Five Senses,* by Melvin and Gilda Berger (Scholastic, 2003) ISBN 978-0439566889

Websites and Other Resources

Student Resources

1. The Brain and Senses
   http://www.childrensuniversity.manchester.ac.uk/interactives/science/brainandsenses

2. Five Senses Game
   http://pbskids.org/sid/isense.html

3. Five Senses Jive
   http://pbskids.org/mamamirabelle/funstuff_videos_five_senses_jive.html

4. Flush the Unhealthy Food Game
   http://www.kscience.co.uk/animations/food.htm

5. Guide Dogs Slideshow
   http://www.slideshare.net/guestb1e4b60/freedom-guide-dogs-for-kids

6. Sense of Taste
   http://library.thinkquest.org/3750/taste/taste.html

7. Sign Design
   http://pbskids.org/arthur/print/signdesign/index.html

8. Unite for Sight
   http://www.uniteforsight.org/kids/about.php

Family Resources

9. United States Department of Health and Human Services
   http://www.hhs.gov

10. Helen Keller
    http://www.afb.org/section.aspx?SectionID=1&TopicID=194

11. Ray Charles
    http://www.pbs.org/wnet/americanmasters/episodes/ray-charles/about-ray-charles/554

Name _____

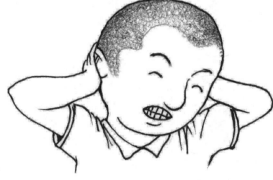

Name _____

Directions: There are two columns of pictures. The left column shows objects that we can sense, and the right column shows the body parts we use to sense these objects. Draw a line from each object to the body part you would use the most to sense it.

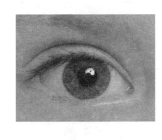

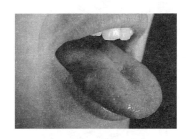

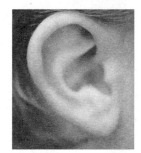

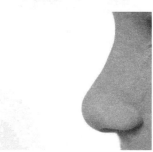

Name _____

Directions: Listen to your teacher's instructions to help you complete the picture of the eye. It is not necessary to label the parts of the eye.

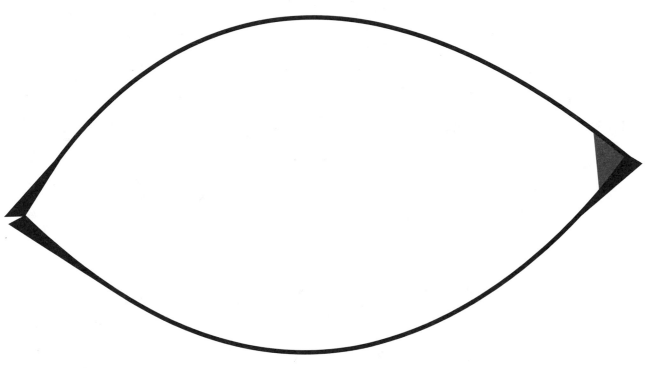

Dear Family Member,

Over the next few days, your child will be learning more about the five senses. S/he will learn about Helen Keller and Ray Charles, two people who overcame disabilities. Ray Charles was a world-renowned musician in spite of the fact that he was blind. Helen Keller, who was both deaf and blind, nonetheless learned how to communicate both by talking and through sign language, as well as how to read and write.

Below are some suggestions for activities that you can do at home to reinforce your child's learning about the five senses.

1. Ray Charles

If possible, buy, borrow, or download some of Ray Charles songs and listen to them with your child. Suggested titles include:

- "Georgia on My Mind"
- "Hit the Road, Jack"
- "You Are My Sunshine"

2. Helen Keller

If possible, rent one of the many videos/DVDs that recount Helen Keller's life and her work with her teacher, Anne Sullivan. Watch the video with your child and talk about the challenges Helen learned to overcome.

3. Words to Use

Below is a list of some of the words that your child will be using at school. Try to use these words as they come up in everyday speech with your child.

- *remarkable*—That is a remarkable drawing!
- *sensations*—Sipping hot chocolate on a cold winter day is one of my favorite sensations.

5. Read Aloud Each Day

It is very important that you read to your child each day. Please refer to the list of books and other resources sent home with the previous family letter, recommending resources related to the five senses.

Be sure to praise your child whenever he/she shares what has been learned at school.

Name _____

1.

2.

3.

4.

5.

6.

7.

8.

9.

10.

Directions: Listen to your teacher's instructions.

11. 😊   ☹

12. 😊   ☹

13. 😊   ☹

14. 😊   ☹

15. 😊   ☹

Name _____

Directions: Listen to your teacher's instructions. Circle all of the sense(s) or body part(s) that would help you discover more about each object pictured. The first one has been done for you.

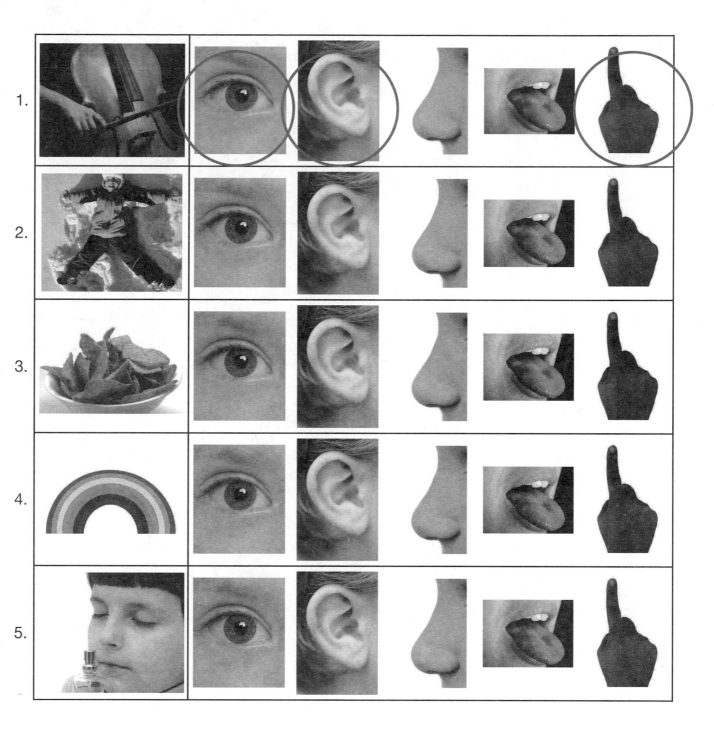

1.

2.

3.

4.

5.

Name _____

Directions: Listen carefully to the situation your teacher reads to you. Circle the sense or body part you would use most to help keep you safe in each situation.

1.

2.

3.

4.

5.

CORE KNOWLEDGE LANGUAGE ARTS

SERIES EDITOR-IN-CHIEF
E. D. Hirsch, Jr.

PRESIDENT
Linda Bevilacqua

EDITORIAL STAFF
Carolyn Gosse, Senior Editor - Preschool
Khara Turnbull, Materials Development Manager
Michelle L. Warner, Senior Editor - Listening & Learning

Mick Anderson
Robin Blackshire
Maggie Buchanan
Paula Coyner
Sue Fulton
Sara Hunt
Erin Kist
Robin Luecke
Rosie McCormick
Cynthia Peng
Liz Pettit
Ellen Sadler
Deborah Samley
Diane Auger Smith
Sarah Zelinke

DESIGN AND GRAPHICS STAFF
Scott Ritchie, Creative Director

Kim Berrall
Michael Donegan
Liza Greene
Matt Leech
Bridget Moriarty
Lauren Pack

CONSULTING PROJECT MANAGEMENT SERVICES
ScribeConcepts.com

ADDITIONAL CONSULTING SERVICES
Ang Blanchette
Dorrit Green
Carolyn Pinkerton

ACKNOWLEDGMENTS

These materials are the result of the work, advice, and encouragement of numerous individuals over many years. Some of those singled out here already know the depth of our gratitude; others may be surprised to find themselves thanked publicly for help they gave quietly and generously for the sake of the enterprise alone. To helpers named and unnamed we are deeply grateful.

CONTRIBUTORS TO EARLIER VERSIONS OF THESE MATERIALS

Susan B. Albaugh, Kazuko Ashizawa, Nancy Braier, Kathryn M. Cummings, Michelle De Groot, Diana Espinal, Mary E. Forbes, Michael L. Ford, Ted Hirsch, Danielle Knecht, James K. Lee, Diane Henry Leipzig, Martha G. Mack, Liana Mahoney, Isabel McLean, Steve Morrison, Juliane K. Munson, Elizabeth B. Rasmussen, Laura Tortorelli, Rachael L. Shaw, Sivan B. Sherman, Miriam E. Vidaver, Catherine S. Whittington, Jeannette A. Williams

We would like to extend special recognition to Program Directors Matthew Davis and Souzanne Wright who were instrumental to the early development of this program.

SCHOOLS

We are truly grateful to the teachers, students, and administrators of the following schools for their willingness to field test these materials and for their invaluable advice: Capitol View Elementary, Challenge Foundation Academy (IN), Community Academy Public Charter School, Lake Lure Classical Academy, Lepanto Elementary School, New Holland Core Knowledge Academy, Paramount School of Excellence, Pioneer Challenge Foundation Academy, New York City PS 26R (The Carteret School), PS 30X (Wilton School), PS 50X (Clara Barton School), PS 96Q, PS 102X (Joseph O. Loretan), PS 104Q (The Bays Water), PS 214K (Michael Friedsam), PS 223Q (Lyndon B. Johnson School), PS 308K (Clara Cardwell), PS 333Q (Goldie Maple Academy), Sequoyah Elementary School, South Shore Charter Public School, Spartanburg Charter School, Steed Elementary School, Thomas Jefferson Classical Academy, Three Oaks Elementary, West Manor Elementary.

And a special thanks to the CKLA Pilot Coordinators Anita Henderson, Yasmin Lugo-Hernandez, and Susan Smith, whose suggestions and day-to-day support to teachers using these materials in their classrooms was critical.

CREDITS

WRITERS

Michael L. Ford, Core Knowledge Staff

ILLUSTRATORS AND IMAGE SOURCES

Take-Home icon: Core Knowledge Staff; 1B-1 (top): Shutterstock; 1B-1 (middle top): Shutterstock; 1B-1 (middle): Shutterstock; 1B-1 (middle bottom): Shutterstock; 1B-1 (bottom): Shutterstock; 3B-1: Steve Morrison; PP1: Shutterstock; PP1 (pointing finger): Shutterstock; PP1 (nose): Shutterstock; PP1 (ear): Shutterstock; PP1 Answer Key: Shutterstock; PP1 Answer Key (pointing finger): Shutterstock; PP1 Answer Key (nose): Shutterstock; PP1 Answer Key (ear): Shutterstock; PP2: Core Knowledge staff; DA-1: Shutterstock; DA-1 (ear): Shutterstock; DA-1 (nose): Shutterstock; DA-1 (pointing finger): Shutterstock; DA-1 Answer Key: Shutterstock; DA-1 Answer Key (ear): Shutterstock; DA-1 Answer Key (nose): Shutterstock; DA-1 Answer Key (pointing finger): Shutterstock; DA-3: Shutterstock; DA-3 (ear): Shutterstock; DA-3 (nose): Shutterstock; DA-3 (pointing finger): Shutterstock; DA-3 Answer Key: Shutterstock; DA-3 Answer Key (ear): Shutterstock; DA-3 Answer Key (nose): Shutterstock; DA-3 Answer Key (pointing finger): Shutterstock

Amplify learning.

Domain 3: Stories
Tell It Again!™ Workbook

Listening & Learning™ Strand
KINDERGARTEN

Core Knowledge®

Name _____

Dear Family Member,

Over the next several days, your child will be learning about classic stories including:

- "Chicken Little"
- "The Three Little Pigs"
- "The Three Billy Goats Gruff"
- "The Wolf and the Seven Little Kids"
- "The Bremen Town Musicians"

Your child will also learn the terms *setting, plot,* and *character* and will use them to talk about the stories s/he will hear. Below are some suggestions for activities that you may do at home to continue to enjoy stories with your child.

1. Words to Use

Below is a list of some of the words that your child will use and learn about from the stories. Try to use these words as they come up in everyday speech with your child.

- *sly* — The sly cat waited for the mouse to look for the cheese.
- *blazing* — Don't look at the blazing hot sun; it will burn your eyes.
- *perched* — Look at that bird perched on the edge of the branch.

2. Character Illustration

Have your child draw a picture of his/her favorite character from a book or story s/he has heard recently. Then have your child explain to you why this character is his or her favorite character.

3. Theater at Home

Encourage your child to retell stories from school. Then, have family members help perform the stories.

4. Read Aloud Each Day

Set aside time to read to your child every day. The local library has many story collections for you to share with your child and a list of books relevant to this topic is attached to this letter.

Be sure to let your child know how much you enjoy hearing about what s/he has been learning about at school.

Recommended Resources for Stories

Trade Book List

1. *The Amazing Bone,* by William Steig (Square Fish, 2011) ISBN 978-0312564216

2. *Brave Wolf and the Thunderbird: Tales of the People,* by Joseph Medicine Crow and illustrated by Linda R. Martin (Abbeville Kids, 1998) ISBN 978-0789201607

3. *Casey Jones,* by Allan Drummond (Farrar Straus and Giroux, 2001) ISBN 978-0374311759

4. *The Fisherman and His Wife,* by Rachel Isadora (Putnam Juvenile, 2008) ISBN 978-0399247712

5. *Hansel and Gretel,* by Rachel Isadora (Putnam Juvenile, 2009) ISBN 978-0399250286

6. *How Chipmunk Got His Stripes,* by Joseph Bruchac and James Bruchac and illustrated by José Aruego and Ariane Dewey (Puffin, 2003) ISBN 978-0142500217

7. *How Many Spots Does a Leopard Have? And Other Tales,* by Julius Lester and illustrated by David Shannon (Scholastic, 1994) ISBN 978-0590419727

8. *The Little Red Hen: An Old Story,* by Margot Zemach (Farrar, Straus, and Giroux, 1993) ISBN 978-0374445119

9. *The Little Red Hen,* by Paul Galdone (Clarion Books, 1985) ISBN 978-0618836840

10. *Little Red Riding Hood,* by Trina Schart Hyman (Holiday House, 1987) ISBN 978-0823406531

11. *Snow White and the Seven Dwarfs: A Tale from the Brothers Grimm,* translated by Randall Jarrell and pictures by Nancy Ekholm Burkert (Farrar, Straus, and Giroux, 1987) ISBN 978-0374468682

12. *The Three Little Javelinas,* by Susan Lowell and illustrated by Jim Harris (Cooper Square, 2009) ISBN 978-0873589550

13. *Three Tuneful Tales (Once-Upon-A-Time),* retold by Marilyn Helmer and illustrated by Kasia Charko (Kids Can Press, 2003) ISBN 978-1550749410

14. *Tikki Tikki Tembo,* by Arlene Mosel and illustrated by Blair Lent (MacMillan, 1998) ISBN 978-0312367480

15. *The Ugly Duckling,* adapted and illustrated by Jerry Pinkney (HarperCollins, 1999) ISBN 978-0688159320

16. *The Velveteen Rabbit (Dover Children's Classics),* by Margery Williams and William Nicholson (Dover Publications, 2011) ISBN 978-0486486062

17. *Why Mosquitoes Buzz in People's Ears: A West African Tale,* by Verna Aardema and pictures by Leo and Diane Dillon (Puffin, 1992) ISBN 978-0140549058

Other Versions of Stories in the Domain

18. *Henny Penny,* by Paul Galdone (Clarion Books, 1984) ISBN 978-0899192253

19. *The Story of Jumping Mouse: A Native American Legend,* retold and illustrated by John Steptoe (HarperTrophy, 1989) ISBN 978-0688087401

20. *The Adventure of Momotaro, the Peach Boy (Kodansha Children's Bilingual Classics),* by Ralph F. McCarthy and illustrated by Ioe Saito (Kodansha International, 2000) ISBN 978-4770020987

21. *The Bremen-Town Musicians,* by Ilse Plume (Dragonfly Books, 1998) ISBN 978-0440414568

22. *Goldilocks and the Three Bears,* by James Marshall (Puffin, 1998) ISBN 978-0140563660

23. *The Three Billy Goats Gruff,* by Paul Galdone (Clarion Books, 1981) ISBN 978-0899190358

Name _____

Directions: Cut out the four pictures. Arrange the pictures in order to show the proper sequence of events. Once they have been sequenced correctly, glue the pictures onto a piece of paper.

Name _____

Directions: Cut out the four pictures. Arrange the pictures in order to show the proper sequence of events. Once they have been sequenced correctly, glue the pictures onto a piece of paper.

Name _____

1.

2.

3.

4.

5.

Dear Family Member,

Over the next several days, your child will enjoy more classic stories including:

- "Momotaro, Peach Boy"
- "The Story of Jumping Mouse"
- "Goldilocks and the Three Bears"
- "Tug-of-War"

Next, your child will review the terms *setting, plot,* and *character* which s/he has been using to talk about the stories s/he has heard. Below are some suggestions for activities that you may do at home to continue to enjoy stories with your child.

1. Words to Use

Below is a list of some of the words that your child will be using and learning about from the stories. Try to use these words as they come up in everyday speech with your child.

- *perilous*—That path looks perilous; let's take a different one.
- *misused*—This hairbrush was misused when someone tried to clean the carpet with it.
- *wee*—That's a wee pebble; you can barely see it.
- *foolishness*—It was pure foolishness to go outside in the cold without a coat.

2. Setting, Characters, Plot Illustration

Have your child draw a picture of the setting of his/her favorite story s/he heard recently. Then have your child draw the characters from the story on the same page. Last, have your child describe the plot or events in the story.

3. Theater at Home

Encourage your child to retell stories from school. Then, have family members help perform the stories.

4. Tug-of-War

Play a game of tug-of-war with your child. Be sure to explain to him or her how the game is won. Relate the game to the story "Tug-of-War" that your child heard in school. Ask your child to describe the plot of the story and who won the tug-of-war in the story.

5. Read Aloud Each Day

It is very important that you read to your child every day. The local library has many story collections for you to share with your child. Please refer to the list of books and other resources sent home with the previous family letter, recommending resources related to these stories.

6. Sayings and Phrases: Do Unto Others As You Would Have Them Do Unto You

Your child will also learn the well-known saying, "do unto others as you would have them do unto you." See if you can find times throughout the day to have your child reflect on this saying.

Be sure to let your child know how much you enjoy hearing about what s/he has been learning about at school.

Name _____

1.

2.

3.

4.

5.

6.

7.

8.

9.

10.

Directions: Listen to your teacher's instructions.

11.

12.

Name _____

Directions: Listen to the teacher's instructions. Next, look at the three pictures in the row and find the one that answers the question. Circle the correct picture.

1.

2.

3.

4.

5.

6.

7.

8.

Name _____

Directions: Draw a line from the characters on the left to their story settings on the right.

CORE KNOWLEDGE LANGUAGE ARTS

SERIES EDITOR-IN-CHIEF
E. D. Hirsch, Jr.

PRESIDENT
Linda Bevilacqua

EDITORIAL STAFF
Carolyn Gosse, Senior Editor - Preschool
Khara Turnbull, Materials Development Manager
Michelle L. Warner, Senior Editor - Listening & Learning

Mick Anderson
Robin Blackshire
Maggie Buchanan
Paula Coyner
Sue Fulton
Sara Hunt
Erin Kist
Robin Luecke
Rosie McCormick
Cynthia Peng
Liz Pettit
Ellen Sadler
Deborah Samley
Diane Auger Smith
Sarah Zelinke

DESIGN AND GRAPHICS STAFF
Scott Ritchie, Creative Director

Kim Berrall
Michael Donegan
Liza Greene
Matt Leech
Bridget Moriarty
Lauren Pack

CONSULTING PROJECT MANAGEMENT SERVICES
ScribeConcepts.com

ADDITIONAL CONSULTING SERVICES
Ang Blanchette
Dorrit Green
Carolyn Pinkerton

ACKNOWLEDGMENTS

These materials are the result of the work, advice, and encouragement of numerous individuals over many years. Some of those singled out here already know the depth of our gratitude; others may be surprised to find themselves thanked publicly for help they gave quietly and generously for the sake of the enterprise alone. To helpers named and unnamed we are deeply grateful.

CONTRIBUTORS TO EARLIER VERSIONS OF THESE MATERIALS

Susan B. Albaugh, Kazuko Ashizawa, Nancy Braier, Kathryn M. Cummings, Michelle De Groot, Diana Espinal, Mary E. Forbes, Michael L. Ford, Ted Hirsch, Danielle Knecht, James K. Lee, Diane Henry Leipzig, Martha G. Mack, Liana Mahoney, Isabel McLean, Steve Morrison, Juliane K. Munson, Elizabeth B. Rasmussen, Laura Tortorelli, Rachael L. Shaw, Sivan B. Sherman, Miriam E. Vidaver, Catherine S. Whittington, Jeannette A. Williams

We would like to extend special recognition to Program Directors Matthew Davis and Souzanne Wright who were instrumental to the early development of this program.

SCHOOLS

We are truly grateful to the teachers, students, and administrators of the following schools for their willingness to field test these materials and for their invaluable advice: Capitol View Elementary, Challenge Foundation Academy (IN), Community Academy Public Charter School, Lake Lure Classical Academy, Lepanto Elementary School, New Holland Core Knowledge Academy, Paramount School of Excellence, Pioneer Challenge Foundation Academy, New York City PS 26R (The Carteret School), PS 30X (Wilton School), PS 50X (Clara Barton School), PS 96Q, PS 102X (Joseph O. Loretan), PS 104Q (The Bays Water), PS 214K (Michael Friedsam), PS 223Q (Lyndon B. Johnson School), PS 308K (Clara Cardwell), PS 333Q (Goldie Maple Academy), Sequoyah Elementary School, South Shore Charter Public School, Spartanburg Charter School, Steed Elementary School, Thomas Jefferson Classical Academy, Three Oaks Elementary, West Manor Elementary.

And a special thanks to the CKLA Pilot Coordinators Anita Henderson, Yasmin Lugo-Hernandez, and Susan Smith, whose suggestions and day-to-day support to teachers using these materials in their classrooms was critical.

CREDITS

Every effort has been taken to trace and acknowledge copyrights. The editors tender their apologies for any accidental infringement where copyright has proved untraceable. They would be pleased to insert the appropriate acknowledgment in any subsequent edition of this publication. Trademarks and trade names are shown in this publication for illustrative purposes only and are the property of their respective owners. The references to trademarks and trade names given herein do not affect their validity.

The Word Work exercises are based on the work of Beck, McKeown, and Kucan in Bringing Words to Life *(The Guilford Press, 2002).*

All photographs are used under license from Shutterstock, Inc. unless otherwise noted.

WRITERS
Rosie McCormick

ILLUSTRATORS AND IMAGE SOURCES
Take-Home Icon: Core Knowledge Staff; 1B-1: Jennifer Eichelberger; 1B-1 Answer Key: Jennifer Eichelberger; 2B-1: Gail McIntosh; 2B-1 Answer Key: Gail McIntosh; 4B-1: Rebecca Miller; 4B-1 Answer Key: Rebecca Miller; PP1 (goats): Mary Parker; PP1 (chicken little): Jennifer Eichelberger; PP1 (mule & farmer): Michael Parker; PP1 (wolf): Core Knowledge Staff; PP1 (wolf at door): Rebecca Miller; PP1 Answer Key (goats): Mary Parker; PP1 Answer Key (chicken little): Jennifer Eichelberger; PP1 Answer Key (mule & farmer): Michael Parker; PP1 Answer Key (wolf): Core Knowledge Staff; PP1 Answer Key (wolf at door): Rebecca Miller; DA-2 (1a): Core Knowledge Staff; DA-2 (1b): Core Knowledge Staff; DA-2 (1c): Core Knowledge Staff; DA-2 (2a): Core Knowledge Staff; DA-2 (2b): Core Knowledge Staff; DA-2 (2c): Shutterstock; DA-2 (3a): Core Knowledge Staff; DA-2 (3b): Core Knowledge Staff; DA-2 (3c): Core Knowledge Staff; DA-2 (4a): Core Knowledge Staff; DA-2 (4b): Jed Henry; DA-2 (4c): Core Knowledge Staff; DA-2 (5a): Shutterstock; DA-2 (5b): Core Knowledge Staff; DA-2 (5c): Core Knowledge Staff; DA-2 (6a): Jed Henry; DA-2 (6b): Jed Henry; DA-2 (6c): Jed Henry; DA-2 (7a): Core Knowledge Staff; DA-2 (7b): Core Knowledge Staff; DA-2 (7c): Core Knowledge Staff; DA-2 (8a): Core Knowledge Staff; DA-2 (8b): Core Knowledge Staff; DA-2 (8c): Core Knowledge Staff; DA-2 Answer Key (1a): Core Knowledge Staff; DA-2 Answer Key (1b): Core Knowledge Staff; DA-2 Answer Key (1c): Core Knowledge Staff; DA-2 Answer Key (2a): Core Knowledge Staff; DA-2 Answer Key (2b): Core Knowledge Staff; DA-2 Answer Key (2c): Shutterstock; DA-2 Answer Key (3a): Core Knowledge Staff; DA-2 Answer Key (3b): Core Knowledge Staff; DA-2 Answer Key (3c): Core Knowledge Staff; DA-2 Answer Key (4a): Core Knowledge Staff; DA-2 Answer Key (4b): Jed Henry; DA-2 Answer Key (4c): Core Knowledge Staff; DA-2 Answer Key (5a): Shutterstock; DA-2 Answer Key (5b): Core Knowledge Staff; DA-2 Answer Key (5c): Core Knowledge Staff; DA-2 Answer Key (6a): Jed Henry; DA-2 Answer Key (6b): Jed Henry; DA-2 Answer Key (6c): Jed Henry; DA-2 Answer Key (7a): Core Knowledge Staff; DA-2 Answer Key (7b): Core Knowledge Staff; DA-2 Answer Key (7c): Core Knowledge Staff; DA-2 Answer Key (8a): Core Knowledge Staff; DA-2 Answer Key (8b): Core Knowledge Staff; DA-2 Answer Key (8c): Core Knowledge Staff; DA-3 (top left): Core Knowledge Staff; DA-3 (top right): Core Knowledge Staff; DA-3 (middle left): Core Knowledge Staff; DA-3 (middle right): Core Knowledge Staff; DA-3 (bottom left): Core Knowledge Staff; DA-3 (bottom right): Core Knowledge Staff

Regarding the Shutterstock items listed above, please note: "No person or entity shall falsely represent, expressly or by way of reasonable implication, that the content herein was created by that person or entity, or any person other than the copyright holder(s) of that content.

Amplify learning.

Domain 4: Plants
Tell It Again!™ Workbook

Listening & Learning™ Strand
KINDERGARTEN

Core Knowledge®

Dear Family Member,

Over the next several days, your child will be learning about plants and plant parts. In addition, your child will learn that plants are living things and that there are many different kinds of plants.

Below are some suggestions for activities that you may do at home to continue to enjoy learning about plants.

1. Plant Experiment

Plant seeds in four different containers. With the first group of seeds, provide no water or sun. With the second group of seeds, provide water, but no sunlight. With the third group of seeds, provide sunlight, but no water. With the fourth group of seeds, provide sun and water. Be sure to explain to your child what you are doing.

Make predictions with your child about which of the seeds will sprout and grow the best. Observe each of the containers every couple of days. Discuss with your child the changes that have taken place, if any. After a week or two, revisit the predictions and discuss with your child whether the predictions were correct and why or why not.

2. Words to Use

Below is a list of some of the words that your child will use and learn about. Try to use these words as the come up in everyday speech with your child.

- *plants*— What do you think about those plants over there?
- *plant*—I think we should plant some flowers in the garden.
- *flowers*—Look at that beautiful flower.
- *soil*—I used a shovel to dig into the soil to plant my flower.

3. Plants Out and About

Any time you are outside with your child, talk with them about the plants you see around you—their size, shape, color, etc. Have your child identify the different plant parts for you.

4. Read Aloud Each Day

Set aside time to read to your child each day. The local library has many nonfiction books about plants, as well as fictional selections. A list of books and other resources relevant to this topic is attached to this letter.

Be sure to let your child know how much you enjoy hearing about what s/he has been learning about at school.

Name _____

Recommended Resources for Plants

Trade Book List

1. *The Boy Who Didn't Believe in Spring,* by Lucille Clifton and illustrated by Brinton Turkle (Puffin, 1992) ISBN 978-0140547399

2. *The Carrot Seed,* by Ruth Krauss and Crockett Johnson (HarperTrophy, 2004) ISBN 978-0064432108

3. *City Green,* by DyAnne DiSalvo-Ryan (HarperCollins, 1994) ISBN 978-0688127862

4. *Daisy (Looking at Life Cycles),* by Victoria Huseby (Smart Apple Media, 2009) ISBN 978-1599201795

5. *Eating the Alphabet: Fruits & Vegetables from A to Z,* by Lois Ehlert (Voyager Books, 1993) ISBN 978-0152244361

6. *The Empty Pot,* by Demi (Henry Holt, 2007) ISBN 978-0805082272

7. *Eyewitness Plant (DK Eyewitness Books),* by David Burnie (DK Publishing, 2011) ISBN 978-0756660352

8. *Flower Garden,* by Eve Bunting and illustrated by Kathryn Hewitt (Voyager Books, 2000) ISBN 978-0152023720

9. *From Bud to Blossom (Apples)*, by Gail Saunders-Smith (Capstone Press, 2006) ISBN 978-1560659518

10. *From Seed to Plant,* by Gail Gibbons (Live Oak Media, 2012) ISBN 978-1430110798

11. *The Great Kapok Tree: A Tale of the Amazon Rainforest,* by Lynne Cherry (Sandpiper, 2000) ISBN 978-0152026141

12. *Growing Vegetable Soup,* by Lois Ehlert (Voyager Books, 1990) ISBN 978-152325800

13. *The Honey Makers,* by Gail Gibbons (HarperTrophy, 2000) ISBN 978-0688175313

14. *How a Seed Grows (Let's-Read-and-Find-Out Science 1),* by Helene J. Jordan and illustrated by Loretta Krupinski (Collins, 1992) ISBN 978-0064451079

15. *I Am a Leaf (Hello Reader! Science, Level 1),* by Jean Marzollo and Judith Moffatt (Cartwheel, 1999) ISBN 978-0590641203

16. *I Am an Apple (Hello Reader! Science, Level 1),* by Jean Marzollo and Judith Moffatt (Scholastic, 1997) ISBN 978-0590372237

17. *I'm a Seed (Hello Reader! Science, Level 1),* by Jean Marzollo and Judith Moffatt (Cartwheel, 1996) ISBN 978-0590265867

18. *Jack's Garden,* by Henry Cole (HarperTrophy, 1997) ISBN 978-0688152833

19. *Johnny Appleseed,* by Reeve Lindbergh and illustrated by Kathy Jakobsen Hallquist (Little, Brown Young Readers, 1993) ISBN 978-0316526340

20. *Johnny Appleseed (Rookie Biographies),* by Christin Ditchfield (Children's Press, 2003) ISBN 978-0516278162

21. *The Life and Times of the Honeybee,* by Charles Micucci (Houghton Mifflin, 1997) ISBN 978-0395861394

22. *The Life and Times of a Peanut,* by Charles Micucci (Houghton Mifflin, 2000) ISBN 978-0618033140

23. *Mama Miti: Wangari Maathai and the Trees of Kenya,* Donna Jo Napoli and illustrated by Kadir Nelson (Simon & Schuster, 2010) ISBN 978-1416935056

24. *Maple Syrup Season,* by Ann Purmell and illustrated by Jill Weber (Holiday House, 2008) ISBN 978-0823418916

25. *Oak Tree (Looking at Life Cycles),* by Victoria Huseby (Smart Apple Media, 2009) ISBN 978-1599201788

26. *OLIVIA Plants a Garden (Olivia Ready-to-Read),* by Emily Sollinger and illustrated by Jared Osterhold (Simon Spotlight, 2011) ISBN 978-1442416758

27. *One Bean,* by Anne Rockwell and pictures by Megan Halsey (Walker Publishing Company, Inc., 1998) ISBN 978-0802775726

28. *Plant a Little Seed,* by Bonnie Christensen (Roaring Brook Press, 2012) ISBN 978-1596435506

29. *Planting a Rainbow,* by Lois Ehlert (Voyager Books, 1992) ISBN 978-0152626105

30. *The Reason for a Flower (Ruth Heller's World of Nature),* by Ruth Heller (Topeka Bindery, 1999) ISBN 978-0833590008

31. *The Seasons of Arnold's Apple Tree,* by Gail Gibbons (Sandpiper, 1988) ISBN 978-0152712457

32. *Seed, Soil, Sun,* by Cris Peterson and photographs by David R. Lundquist (Boyds Mills Press, 2010) ISBN 978-1590787137

33. *Soil Basics/Lo Básico de la Tierra,* by Carol Lindeen (Capstone, 2010) ISBN 978-1429653473

34. *The Tiny Seed (The World of Eric Carle),* by Eric Carle (Aladdin, 2001) ISBN 978-0689842443

35. *Wangari's Trees of Peace: A True Story from Africa,* by Jeanette Winter (Harcourt, 2008) ISBN 978-0152065454

36. *Why Do Leaves Change Color? (Let's-Read-and-Find-Out Science, Stage 2),* by Betsy Maestro and illustrated by Loretta Krupinski (HarperCollins, 1994) ISBN 978-0064451260

Note: This book is more appropriate for individualized reading.

Websites and Other Resources

Student Resources

1. Parts of Plant Game
http://www.softschools.com/science/plants/plant_parts/

2. Plant Games
http://www.cookie.com/kids/games/grow-plant.html

3. "Groovy Garden" Game
http://pbskids.org/arthur/games/groovygarden/groovygarden.html

4.   George Washington Carver
     http://www.ideafinder.com/history/inventors/carver.htm

5.   "Biology of Plants"
     http://www.mbgnet.net/bioplants/main.html

Name _____

Directions: The worksheet shows the parts of a plant. Cut out and paste the parts to make a whole plant.

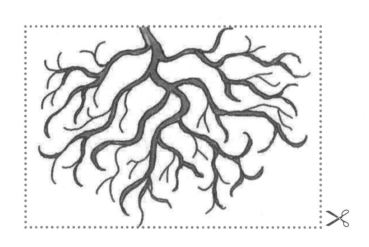

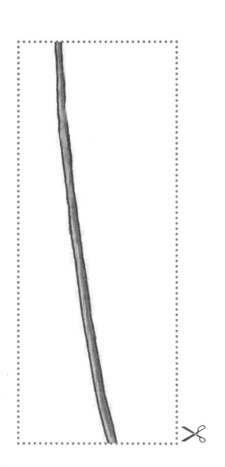

Directions: Color the pictures of the turnip at various stages, then cut them out. Sequence the pictures, starting with the beginning of the turnip's life cycle and finishing with the picture that demonstrates the end of the turnip's life cycle. Last, glue the pictures in the correct order onto a separate sheet of paper.

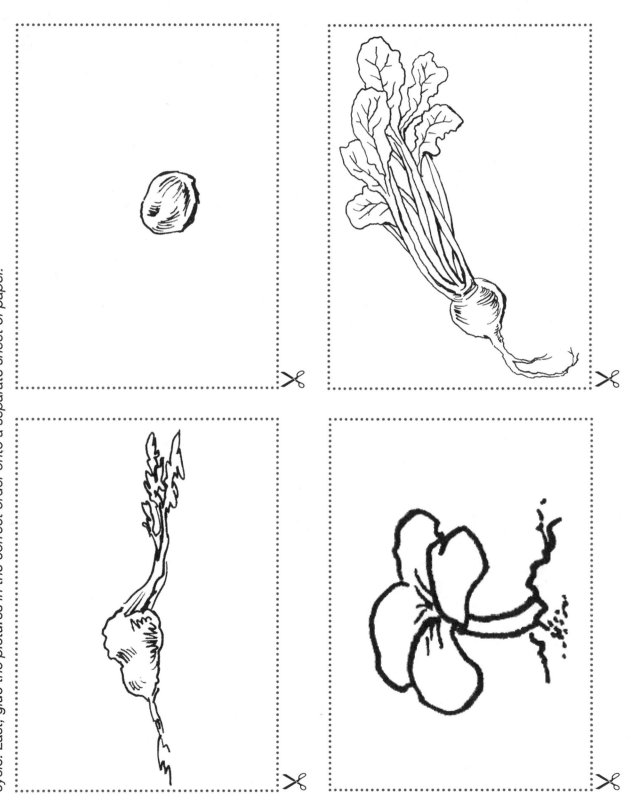

Directions: The worksheet shows the stem of a plant growing out of the earth. Draw in and color the other parts of the plant.

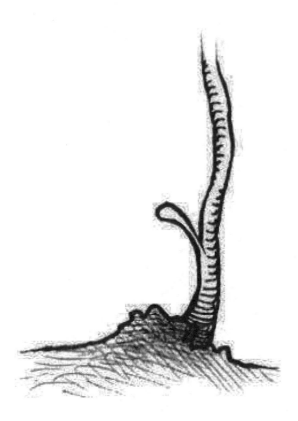

Dear Family Member,

Over the past several days, your child has been learning about plants, plant parts, and pollination. Your child will soon learn about germination, the difference between deciduous and evergreen trees, interesting plants, plants and people, and George Washington Carver.

Below are some suggestions for activities that you may do at home to continue to enjoy learning about plants.

1. Leaf Rubbings

If possible, collect a number of different types of leaves. Have your child compare and contrast the different types of leaves—size, color, shape, etc. Have him or her make a rubbing of the leaves by placing a sheet of paper over the leaves and gently rubbing the paper with the side of a pencil or crayon.

2. Words to Use

Below is a list of some of the words that your child will use and learn about. Try to use these words as they come up in everyday speech with your child.

- *fruit*—The apple you are eating is a fruit.

- *deciduous*—That is a deciduous plant; it loses its leaves in the fall.

- *evergreen*—That evergreen tree keeps its leaves all year!

- *bouquet*—Isn't that a pretty bouquet? It is so nice to receive a bunch of flowers!

3. All About Roots

One way to illustrate roots for your child is to buy seedlings and shake away the dirt to reveal the root system.

4. Plants as Food

While eating with your child, explain which parts of the meal come from plants and identify those plants by name. Also, tell your child which part of the plant the food comes from. You may wish to talk about which plants are considered fruits and which plants are considered vegetables. The chart below shows commonly eaten foods and the plant parts they come from:

Roots	Stems	Leaves	Seeds	Flowers	Fruits
potato	celery	lettuce	wheat	cauliflower	apple
carrot	sugar cane	cabbage	corn	broccoli	tomato
beet	asparagus	spinach	rice		orange
radish		parsley	beans		
turnip		basil	oats		
			barley		

5. Read Aloud Each Day

Set aside time to read to your child each day. The local library has many nonfiction books about plants, as well as fictional selections. Please refer to the list of books and other resources sent home with the previous family letter, recommending resources related to plants.

6. Sayings and Phrases: Great Oaks from Little Acorns Grow

Your child will also learn the well-known saying "great oaks from little acorns grow." Things or people that may seem small and insignificant at first can often turn into something or someone important. You may wish to find opportunities to apply this saying for your child.

Be sure to let your child know how much you enjoy hearing about what s/he has been learning about at school.

Name _____

Directions: Think about how a deciduous apple tree looks in each season: spring, summer, fall, and winter. Think about how you can show this in a picture with the parts of the tree and with different colors. Decorate the trees to show the seasons.

Name _____

Directions: With your teacher's help, match each item on the left with the plant that it comes from on the right.

1.

2.

3.

4.

5.

Name _____

1.

2.

3.

4.

5.

6.

7.

8.

9.

10.

Directions: Listen to your teacher's instructions.

11. 🙂 ☹️

12. 🙂 ☹️

13. 🙂 ☹️

14. 🙂 ☹️

15. 🙂 ☹️

Name _____

Directions: Listen to your teacher's instructions.

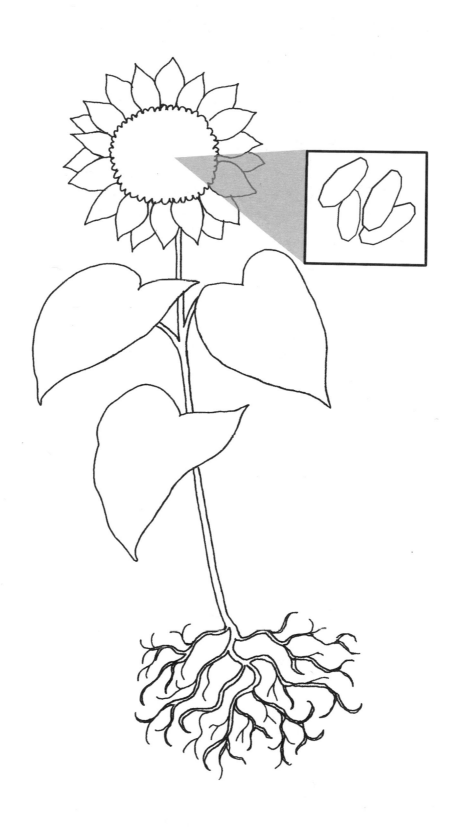

Name _____

1.

2.

Directions: Listen to your teacher's instructions.

Name _____

1.

2.

3.

4.

5.

Core Knowledge Language Arts

Series Editor-in-Chief
E. D. Hirsch, Jr.

President
Linda Bevilacqua

Editorial Staff
Carolyn Gosse, Senior Editor - Preschool
Khara Turnbull, Materials Development Manager
Michelle L. Warner, Senior Editor - Listening & Learning

Mick Anderson
Robin Blackshire
Maggie Buchanan
Paula Coyner
Sue Fulton
Sara Hunt
Erin Kist
Robin Luecke
Rosie McCormick
Cynthia Peng
Liz Pettit
Ellen Sadler
Deborah Samley
Diane Auger Smith
Sarah Zelinke

Design and Graphics Staff
Scott Ritchie, Creative Director

Kim Berrall
Michael Donegan
Liza Greene
Matt Leech
Bridget Moriarty
Lauren Pack

Consulting Project Management Services
ScribeConcepts.com

Additional Consulting Services
Ang Blanchette
Dorrit Green
Carolyn Pinkerton

Acknowledgments

These materials are the result of the work, advice, and encouragement of numerous individuals over many years. Some of those singled out here already know the depth of our gratitude; others may be surprised to find themselves thanked publicly for help they gave quietly and generously for the sake of the enterprise alone. To helpers named and unnamed we are deeply grateful.

Contributors to Earlier Versions of these Materials
Susan B. Albaugh, Kazuko Ashizawa, Nancy Braier, Kathryn M. Cummings, Michelle De Groot, Diana Espinal, Mary E. Forbes, Michael L. Ford, Ted Hirsch, Danielle Knecht, James K. Lee, Diane Henry Leipzig, Martha G. Mack, Liana Mahoney, Isabel McLean, Steve Morrison, Juliane K. Munson, Elizabeth B. Rasmussen, Laura Tortorelli, Rachael L. Shaw, Sivan B. Sherman, Miriam E. Vidaver, Catherine S. Whittington, Jeannette A. Williams

We would like to extend special recognition to Program Directors Matthew Davis and Souzanne Wright who were instrumental to the early development of this program.

Schools
We are truly grateful to the teachers, students, and administrators of the following schools for their willingness to field test these materials and for their invaluable advice: Capitol View Elementary, Challenge Foundation Academy (IN), Community Academy Public Charter School, Lake Lure Classical Academy, Lepanto Elementary School, New Holland Core Knowledge Academy, Paramount School of Excellence, Pioneer Challenge Foundation Academy, New York City PS 26R (The Carteret School), PS 30X (Wilton School), PS 50X (Clara Barton School), PS 96Q, PS 102X (Joseph O. Loretan), PS 104Q (The Bays Water), PS 214K (Michael Friedsam), PS 223Q (Lyndon B. Johnson School), PS 308K (Clara Cardwell), PS 333Q (Goldie Maple Academy), Sequoyah Elementary School, South Shore Charter Public School, Spartanburg Charter School, Steed Elementary School, Thomas Jefferson Classical Academy, Three Oaks Elementary, West Manor Elementary.

And a special thanks to the CKLA Pilot Coordinators Anita Henderson, Yasmin Lugo-Hernandez, and Susan Smith, whose suggestions and day-to-day support to teachers using these materials in their classrooms was critical.

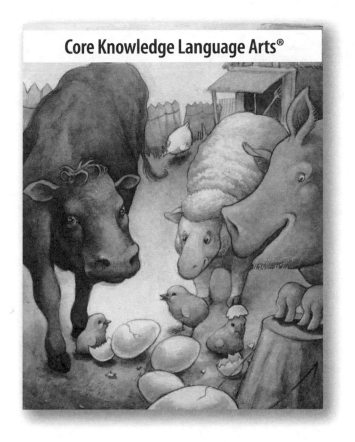

Domain 5: Farms

Tell it Again!™ Workbook

Listening & Learning™ Strand

KINDERGARTEN

Amplify learning.

Core Knowledge®

Dear Family Member,

Are you familiar with the song, "Old MacDonald Had a Farm"? If not, have your child teach it to you! During the next two weeks, your child will be learning about farms. The focus for the first several days will be farm animals, specifically cows, chickens, pigs, and sheep. Your child will learn farm animal names and the sounds that these animals make. S/he will learn that farm animals need food, water, and space to live and grow, and will learn why farmers raise animals. Your child will understand that farmers work very hard to provide food for us.

Below are some suggestions for activities that you may do at home to reinforce what has been learned at school.

1. Search for Farm Pictures

Look through books or magazines for pictures of animals. First, ask your child if the animal lives on a farm or not. If the animal is a farm animal, ask your child if s/he can name the animal and make the sound that the animal makes. Also, talk with your child about what the farm animal needs—food, water, and shelter—and how the farmer provides these needs.

2. Identify Foods from Farms

When you are grocery shopping, or preparing or eating a meal, talk with your child about the foods that came from a farm. Over the next few days, they will learn about dairy, beef, chicken, and pork products. (Note: You may want to explain to/remind your child that for different reasons, some people do not eat eggs, dairy, or meat.)

3. Draw a Farm

Have your child draw or paint a picture of a farm or one of the farm animals and then tell you about it. Again, ask questions to keep your child using the vocabulary that s/he has learned.

4. Visit a Farm or Farmers' Market

See if there is a farm in your community that you may visit with your child to learn more about farms. If not, a farmer's market is another great option. Also, talk about any farms and the barns, tractors, pastures, and farm animals that you might pass when you are going to various places.

5. Read Aloud Each Day

It is very important that you read to your child every day. The local library has both fiction and nonfiction books about farms and farm animals that you may share with your child. A list of books and other relevant resources is attached to this letter.

6. Sayings and Phrases: The Early Bird Gets the Worm

Your child will also learn the well-known saying, "the early bird gets the worm." Farmers are certainly early birds. Ask your child if s/he can think of good things or rewards that come from being early. Find opportunities to use this saying when your child is or is not being the "early bird."

Be sure to let your child know how much you enjoy hearing about what s/he has learned at school.

Recommended Resources for Farms

Trade Books

1. *Barnyard Banter,* by Denise Fleming (Henry Holt and Company, 2008) ISBN 978-0805087789

2. *Bee-bim Bop!,* by Linda Sue Park and illustrated by Ho Baek Lee (Sandpiper, Houghton Mifflin Harcourt, 2008) ISBN 978-0547076713

3. *The Cazuela that the Farm Maiden Stirred,* by Samantha R. Vamos and illustrated by Rafael Lopez (Charlesbridge Publishing, 2011) ISBN 978-1580892421

4. *Chicken Dance,* by Tammi Sauer and illustrated by Dan Santat (Sterling, 2009) ISBN 978-1402753664

5. *Chicken Soup,* by Jean Van Leeuwen and illustrated by David Gavril (Abrams Books for Young Readers, 2009) ISBN 978-0810983267

6. *Chickens (Farmyard Friends),* by Camilla de la Bédoyère (QEB Publishing, 2010) ISBN 978-1595669421

7. *Chicks & Chickens,* by Gail Gibbons (Holiday House, 2005) ISBN 978-0823419395

8. *Clarabelle: Making Milk and So Much More,* by Cris Peterson (Boyds Mills Press, 2007) ISBN 978-1590783108

9. *Click, Clack, Moo: Cows That Type,* by Doreen Cronin and illustrated by Betsy Lewin (Atheneum Books for Young Readers, 2000) ISBN 978-1416903482

10. *Cycle of Rice, Cycle of Life: A Story of Sustainable Farming,* by Jan Reynolds (Lee & Low Books, 2009) ISBN 978-1600602542

11. *Daisy Comes Home,* by Jan Brett (Penguin Group, 2005) ISBN 978-0142402702

12. *A Day in the Life of a Farmer,* by Heather Adamson (Capstone Press, 2006) ISBN 978-0736846745

13. *Fantastic Farm Machines,* by Cris Peterson and David R. Lundquist (Boyds Mill Press, 2006) ISBN 978-1590782712

14. *Farm,* by Elisha Cooper (Orchard Books, 2010) ISBN 978-0545070751

15. *Farming,* by Gail Gibbons (Holiday House, 1990) ISBN 978-0823407972

16. *Farms around the World (World of Farming)*, by Catherine Veitch (Heinemann-Raintree, 2011) ISBN 978-1432954987

17. *Food from Farms,* by Nancy Dickmann (Heinemann-Raintree, 2010) ISBN 978-1432939434

18. *From Seed to Pumpkin,* by Wendy Pfeffer (HarperCollins, 2004) ISBN 978-0064451909

19. *Grandpa's Tractor,* by Michael Garland (Boyds Mills Press, 2011) ISBN 978-1590787625

20. *Growing Vegetable Soup,* by Lois Ehlert (Voyager Books, 1990) ISBN 978-0152325800

21. *Harvesters (Farm Machines),* by Connor Dayton (Powerkids Pr, 2011) ISBN 978-1448850464

22. *If You Give a Pig a Pancake,* by Laura Numeroff and illustrated by Felicia Bond (HarperCollins, 1998) ISBN 978-0060266868

23. *Jobs on a Farm,* by Nancy Dickmann (Heinemann-Raintree, 2010) ISBN 978-1432939458

24. *Life on a Crop Farm,* by Judy Wolfman and David Lorenz Winston (Carolrhoda Books, 2001) ISBN 978-1575055183

25. *Life on a Dairy Farm,* by Judy Wolfman and David Lorenz Winston (Carolrhoda Books, 2004) ISBN 978-1575051901

26. *The Life of Rice: From Seedling to Supper (Traveling Photographer)*, by Richard Sobol (Candlewick, 2010) ISBN 978-0763632526

27. *The Little Red Hen,* by Paul Galdone (Houghton Mifflin Harcourt, 2011) ISBN 978-0547370187

28. *A Mango in the Hand: A Story Told Through Proverbs,* by Antonio Sacre and illustrated by Sebastia Serra (Abrams Books for Young Readers, 2011) ISBN 978-0810997349

29. *Market Day,* by Carol Foskett Cordsen and illustrated by Douglas B. Jones (Dutton Children's Books, 2008) ISBN 978-0525478836

30. *The Milk Makers,* by Gail Gibbons (Aladdin, 1987) ISBN 978-0689711169

31. *One Hen: How One Small Loan Made a Big Difference,* by Katie Smith Milway and illustrated by Eugenie Fernandes (Kids Can Press, 2008) ISBN 978-1554530281

32. *On the Farm,* by David Elliott and illustrated by Holly Meade (Candlewick, 2012) ISBN 978-0763655914

33. *On Ramón's Farm: Five Tales of Mexico,* by Campbell Geeslin and illustrated by Petra Mathers (Atheneum/Anne Schwartz Book, 1998) ISBN 978-0689811340

34. *Ox-Cart Man,* by Donald Hall and illustrated by Barbara Cooney (Puffin, 1983) ISBN 978-0140504415

35. *A Picture Book of César Chávez,* by David A. Adler and Michael S. Adler, and illustrated by Mary Olofsdotter (Holiday House, 2011) ISBN 978-0823423835

36. *The Princess and the Pig,* by Jonathan Emmet and illustrated by Poly Bernatene (Walker & Co., 2011) ISBN 978-0802723345

37. *Pigs,* by Gail Gibbons (Holiday House, 2000) ISBN 978-0823415540

38. *The Rusty, Trusty Tractor,* by Joy Cowley and illustrated by Olivier Dunrea (Boyd's Mills Press, 2000) ISBN 978-1563978739

39. *Sip, Slurp, Soup, Soup/Caldo, Caldo, Caldo,* by Diane Gonzales Bertrand and illustrated by Alex Pardo Delange (Arte Publico Press, 2008) ISBN 978-1558852419

40. *Some Pig! A Charlotte's Web Picture Book,* by E.B. White and illustrated by Maggie Kneen (Stirling, 2009) ISBN 978-1435116399

41. *The Year at Maple Hill Farm,* by Alice and Martin Provensen (Aladdin, 2001) ISBN 978-0689845000

42. *To Market, To Market,* by Nikki McClure (Abram Books for Young Readers, 2011) ISBN 978-0810997387

43. *Yum! Mmmm! Qué rico! America's Sproutings,* by Pat Mora and Rafael Lopez (Lee & Low Books, 2007) ISBN 978-1584302711

Websites and Other Resources

Student Resources

1. Animal Sounds Video
   http://bit.ly/TOeCyZ

2. Planting Game
   http://pbskids.org/sid/fablab_vegetableplanting.html

Family Resources

3. Farm Machines
   http://www.kidcyber.com.au/topics/farmmachines.htm

4. History of Farming
   http://inventors.about.com/library/inventors/blfarm1.htm

5. Farm Museum
   http://queensfarm.org/our-animals.html

⑩ Recording Sheet for Recitation of "Old MacDonald Had a Farm" Assessment

Note: You will want to find a time for each student to to recite "Old MacDonald Had a Farm" for you or the class. Use this recording sheet to document this assessment.

Student's Name _____

Date _____

Title of Nursery Rhyme _____

Scoring: _____

10 Recited entire song correctly

5   Recited some lines of the song correctly

1   Was not able to recite any lines of the song correctly

Comments _____

_____

_____

_____

_____

Dear Family Member,

I hope that you have been having fun doing activities at home to learn about farms and farm animals. The focus for the next several days will be farm crops. Your child will learn crop names, what farmers need to provide so that the crops will live and grow, and why farmers raise crops. S/he will learn what happens on a farm during each of the four seasons—planting, growing, and harvesting. Your child will continue to learn that farmers work very hard to provide food for us and how that food gets from the farm to the market. Your child will also enjoy listening to *The Little Red Hen,* the fictional story of a well-known farmer.

Below are some suggestions for activities that you can do at home to reinforce what has been learned at school.

1. Search for Farm Pictures

Look through books or magazines for pictures of farms and farm crops. Ask your child if s/he can name the crop and how the crop may be used. Also, talk with your child about what the crop needs—food, water, and pest control— and how the farmer provides these.

2. Identify Foods from Farms

When you are grocery shopping, or preparing or eating a meal, talk with your child about the foods that came from farm crops. They will learn about fruits, vegetables, and foods made from grains such as bread, cereal, and pasta.

3. Draw a Farm

Have your child draw or paint a picture of a farm with crops and then tell you about it. Again, ask questions to keep your child using the vocabulary that s/he has learned.

4. Visit a Farm or Farmers' Market

See if there is a farm in your community that you may visit with your child to learn more about farms. If not, a farmer's market is another great option. Also, talk about any farms and the barns, tractors, pastures, and farm animals that you might pass when you are going to various places.

5. Read Aloud Each Day

It is very important that you read to your child every day. The local library has both fiction and nonfiction books about farms and farm crops that you may share with your child. Refer to the list sent home with the last family letter.

Be sure to let your child know how much you enjoy hearing about what s/he has learned at school.

Name _____

Directions: The pictures on the worksheet show some of the events of "The Little Red Hen". Look at each picture and think about what is happening. Cut out the pictures and put them in order to show the events of the story from beginning to end. Retell the story using the pictures. When you are sure that you have them in the correct order, glue them on a separate sheet of paper in the correct order.

Name _____

Directions: The pictures on the worksheet show some of the events that take place to get food from the farm to the market. Look at each picture and think about what is happening. Cut out the pictures and arrange them to show the order of events. Retell the events using the pictures. When you are sure that you have them in the correct order, glue them on a separate sheet of paper in the correct order.

Name _____

Directions: Listen carefully to the words and sentences read by your teacher. If the sentence uses the word correctly, circle the smiling face. If the sentence uses the word incorrectly, circle the frowning face.

1.

2. ☺ ☹

3. ☺ ☹

4.

5. ☺ ☹

6.

7.

8. ☺ ☹

9.

10. ☺ ☹

11. 🙂 ☹

12. 🙂 ☹

13. 🙂 ☹

14. 🙂 ☹

Name _____

Directions: Circle the picture that answers each question about farms.

1.

2.

3.

4.

5.

6.

7.

8.

9.

10.

CORE KNOWLEDGE LANGUAGE ARTS

SERIES EDITOR-IN-CHIEF
E. D. Hirsch, Jr.

PRESIDENT
Linda Bevilacqua

EDITORIAL STAFF
Carolyn Gosse, Senior Editor - Preschool
Khara Turnbull, Materials Development Manager
Michelle L. Warner, Senior Editor - Listening & Learning

Mick Anderson
Robin Blackshire
Maggie Buchanan
Paula Coyner
Sue Fulton
Sara Hunt
Erin Kist
Robin Luecke
Rosie McCormick
Cynthia Peng
Liz Pettit
Ellen Sadler
Deborah Samley
Diane Auger Smith
Sarah Zelinke

DESIGN AND GRAPHICS STAFF
Scott Ritchie, Creative Director

Kim Berrall
Michael Donegan
Liza Greene
Matt Leech
Bridget Moriarty
Lauren Pack

CONSULTING PROJECT MANAGEMENT SERVICES
ScribeConcepts.com

ADDITIONAL CONSULTING SERVICES
Ang Blanchette
Dorrit Green
Carolyn Pinkerton

ACKNOWLEDGMENTS

These materials are the result of the work, advice, and encouragement of numerous individuals over many years. Some of those singled out here already know the depth of our gratitude; others may be surprised to find themselves thanked publicly for help they gave quietly and generously for the sake of the enterprise alone. To helpers named and unnamed we are deeply grateful.

CONTRIBUTORS TO EARLIER VERSIONS OF THESE MATERIALS

Susan B. Albaugh, Kazuko Ashizawa, Nancy Braier, Kathryn M. Cummings, Michelle De Groot, Diana Espinal, Mary E. Forbes, Michael L. Ford, Ted Hirsch, Danielle Knecht, James K. Lee, Diane Henry Leipzig, Martha G. Mack, Liana Mahoney, Isabel McLean, Steve Morrison, Juliane K. Munson, Elizabeth B. Rasmussen, Laura Tortorelli, Rachael L. Shaw, Sivan B. Sherman, Miriam E. Vidaver, Catherine S. Whittington, Jeannette A. Williams

We would like to extend special recognition to Program Directors Matthew Davis and Souzanne Wright who were instrumental to the early development of this program.

SCHOOLS

We are truly grateful to the teachers, students, and administrators of the following schools for their willingness to field test these materials and for their invaluable advice: Capitol View Elementary, Challenge Foundation Academy (IN), Community Academy Public Charter School, Lake Lure Classical Academy, Lepanto Elementary School, New Holland Core Knowledge Academy, Paramount School of Excellence, Pioneer Challenge Foundation Academy, New York City PS 26R (The Carteret School), PS 30X (Wilton School), PS 50X (Clara Barton School), PS 96Q, PS 102X (Joseph O. Loretan), PS 104Q (The Bays Water), PS 214K (Michael Friedsam), PS 223Q (Lyndon B. Johnson School), PS 308K (Clara Cardwell), PS 333Q (Goldie Maple Academy), Sequoyah Elementary School, South Shore Charter Public School, Spartanburg Charter School, Steed Elementary School, Thomas Jefferson Classical Academy, Three Oaks Elementary, West Manor Elementary.

And a special thanks to the CKLA Pilot Coordinators Anita Henderson, Yasmin Lugo-Hernandez, and Susan Smith, whose suggestions and day-to-day support to teachers using these materials in their classrooms was critical.

 Core Knowledge®

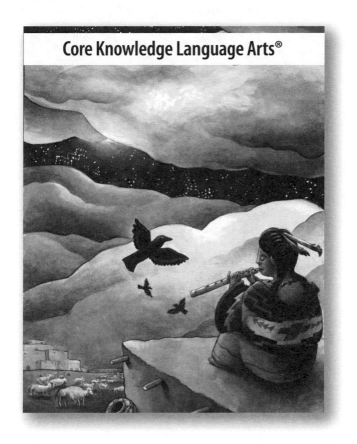

Core Knowledge Language Arts®

Domain 6: Native Americans
Tell It Again!™ Workbook

Listening & Learning™ Strand
KINDERGARTEN

Amplify learning.

Core Knowledge®

Dear Family Member,

Over the next several days, your child will be learning about different Native American tribes and the ways they lived long ago. S/he will learn that there were many, many tribes in many different regions of the country. The focus of this domain will be upon three tribes: the Lakota Sioux, the Wampanoag, and the Lenape. The Lakota Sioux settled in the Great Plains region of the United States, while both the Wampanoag and the Lenape lived in the Eastern Woodlands region. These tribes have been chosen to provide a clear comparison of daily life among Native Americans, including:

- how they lived;

- what they wore and ate; and

- what their homes were like.

Below are some suggestions for activities that you may do at home to reinforce what your child is learning about the Native Americans of long ago.

1. Where Are We?

Help your child locate the Great Plains (North and South Dakota, Nebraska, Wyoming, Montana, Oklahoma, Texas, Colorado) and the Eastern Woodlands (particularly Rhode Island, Massachusetts, and New York) on a U.S. map. Share any knowledge you have of these areas. Point out on the map where you live.

2. Words to Use

Below is a list of some of the words that your child will use and learn about. Try to use these words as they come up in everyday speech with your child.

- *tribes*—There are many different Native American tribes, each with their own culture and traditions.

- *shelter*—The tent gave us shelter from the storm.

- *agile*—The agile gymnast performed on the balance beam.

- *mischief*—My little sister likes to get into mischief by hiding all my favorite books.

- *succulent*—The strawberries we picked off the vine were succulent.

3. If You Were There

With your child, imagine what it would have been like to live without any of our modern conveniences, having to depend upon the environment for food, clothing, and shelter. Talk about what you would have seen and heard and how you would have felt.

4. Read Aloud Each Day

It is very important that you read to your child each day. The local library has many books on Native Americans and a list of books and other resources relevant to this topic is attached to this letter.

Be sure to praise your child whenever s/he shares what has been learned at school.

Recommended Trade Books for Native Americans

Trade Book List

General

1. *D is for Drum: A Native American Alphabet,* by Michael and Debbie Shoulders and illustrated by Irving Toddy (Sleeping Bear Press, 2011) ISBN 978-1585362745

2. *Many Nations: An Alphabet of Native America*, by Joseph Bruchac and illustrated by Robert F. Goetzl (Troll Communications, 1998) ISBN 978-0816744602

3. *Native Americans*, edited by E. D. Hirsch, Jr. (Pearson Learning, 2002) ISBN 978-0769050010

4. *The Story of Jumping Mouse: A Native American Legend*, by John Steptoe (HarperTrophy, 1989) ISBN 978-0688087401

Tribes Discussed in the Domain

5. *Clambake: A Wampanoag Tradition*, by Russell M. Peters and photographs by John Madama (Lerner Publications Company, 1992) ISBN 978-0822596219

6. *If You Lived with the Sioux Indians*, by Ann McGovern and illustrated by Jean Drew (Scholastic, Inc., 1992) ISBN 978-0590451628

7. *The Legend of the Indian Paintbrush,* by Tomie dePaola (Puffin, 1996) ISBN 978-0698113602

8. *The Sioux*, by Alice Osinski (Children's Press, 1984) ISBN 978-0516019291*

9. *Squanto and the First Thanksgiving,* by Eric Metaxas and illustrated by Michael Donato (Rabbit Ears Books, 2012) ISBN 978-1575055855

10. *Tapenum's Day: A Wampanoag Indian Boy in Pilgrim Times*, by Kate Waters and photographs by Russ Kendall (Scholastic, Inc., 1996) ISBN 978-0590202374

11. *The Wampanoags*, by Alice K. Flanagan (Children's Press, 1998) ISBN 978-0516263885

12. *When the Shadbush Blooms*, by Carla Messinger and Susan Katz and illustrated by David Kanietakeron Fadden (Tricycle Press, 2007) ISBN 978-1582461922

Supplementary Reading, Tribes Not Discussed in the Domain

13. *Buffalo Bird Girl: A Hidatsa Story,* by S.D. Nelson (Abrams Books for Young Readers, 2012) ISBN 978-1419703553

14. *Coyote: A Trickster Tale from the American Southwest*, retold and illustrated by Gerald McDermott (Voyager, 1999) ISBN 978-0152019587

15. *How the Stars Fell into the Sky: A Navajo Legend,* by Jerrie Oughton and illustrated by Lisa Desimini (Sandpiper, 1996) ISBN 978-0395779385

16. *If You Lived with the Hopi,* by Anne Kamma and illustrated by Linda Gardner (Scholastic, Inc., 1999) ISBN 978-0590397261

17. *If You Lived with the Indians of the Northwest Coast,* by Anne Kamma and illustrated by Pamela Johnson (Scholastic Inc., 2002) ISBN 978-0439260770

18. *If You Lived with the Iroquois,* by Ellen Levine and illustrated by Shelly Hehenberger (Scholastic, Inc., 1998) ISBN 978-0590674454

19. *The Legend of the Bluebonnet,* by Tomie dePaola (Penguin Putnam Books for Young Readers, 1996) ISBN 978-0698113596

20. *Raven: A Trickster Tale from the Pacific Northwest,* by Gerald McDermott (Harcourt, 1993) ISBN 978-0152656614

21. *Totem Tale: A Tall Story from Alaska,* by Deb Vanasse and illustrated by Erik Brooks (Sasquatch Books, 2006) ISBN 978-1570614392

Native Americans Today

22. *Children of Native America Today,* by Yvonne Wakim Dennis and Arlene B. Hirschfelder (Charlesbridge, 2003) ISBN 978-1570914997

23. *Jingle Dancer,* by Cynthia Leitich Smith and illustrated by Cornelius Van Wright and Ying-Hwa Hu (Morrow Junior Books, 2000) ISBN 978-0688162412

24. *Meet Lydia: A Native Girl from Southeast Alaska (My World: Young Native Americans Today),* by Miranda Belarde-Lewis and photographs by John Harrington (Council Oak Books, 2004) ISBN 978-1571781475

25. *Meet Mindy: A Native Girl from the Southwest (My World: Young Native Americans Today),* by Susan Secakuku and photographs by John Harrington (Council Oak Books, 2006) ISBN 978-1571781482

26. *Meet Naiche: A Native Boy from the Chesapeake Bay Region (My World: Young Native Americans Today),* by Gabrielle Tayac and photographs by John Harrington (Council Oak Books, 2007) ISBN 978-1571781468*

27. *Songs from the Loom: A Navajo Girl Learns to Weave (We Are Still Here: Native Americans Today),* by Monty Roessel (Lerner Publishing Group, 1995) ISBN 978-0822597124

***Note:** These books contain a great deal of pertinent information but may be above grade level. Feel free to read sections of these books as you see fit.

Websites and Other Resources

Student Resources

1. National Museum of the American Indian
   http://nmai.si.edu/visit/newyork/

2. Native American Homes
   http://www.native-languages.org/houses.htm

Family Resources

3. Map of Native American Tribes
   http://images.wikia.com/oraltradition/images/d/dc/Native_American_Tribes_Map_2.jpg

4. Native American Environment
   http://cpluhna.nau.edu/Research/native_americans1.htm

5.   Pictures of Native Americans
   http://kids.nationalgeographic.com/kids/photos/native-americans/#/100
   3043_14107_600x450.jpg

6.   Wampanoag Tribe
   http://www.indians.org/articles/wampanoag-indians.html

Directions: Circle the items that might have been made from parts of the buffalo.

Name _____

Directions: 1. Draw a picture of the kind of house in which the Lakota Sioux lived. 2. Draw a picture of what the Lakota Sioux ate. 3. Finish the picture of the Lakota Sioux Native American by "dressing" the figure in typical Sioux clothing. You may choose to make the figure either a boy or a girl.

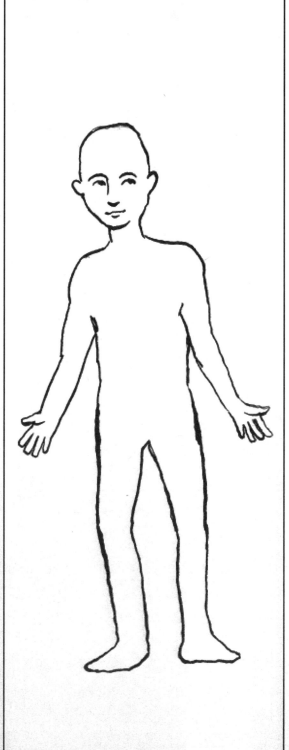

Dear Family Member,

I hope your child has enjoyed learning about the Lakota Sioux Native American tribe. Over the next several days, your child will be learning about the Wampanoag and Lenape tribes, as well as Native American tribes today. It is important for all of us to recognize the past, but it is equally important to acknowledge the present.

Below are some suggestions for activities that you may do at home to reinforce the fact that Native Americans are one of the many groups of people that contribute to America's diversity today.

1. Native American Neighbors

What Native American tribes are represented in your area today? Is there a way that you can find out more about them? Do they hold powwows, host educational events, or share knowledge with the larger community? Do some research with your child to find out.

2. Words to Use

Below is a list of some of the words that your child will use and learn about. Try to use these words as the come up in everyday speech with your child.

- *feasts* — At Thanksgiving, my family feasts on turkey, mashed potatoes, green beans, corn, and pumpkin pie.

- *harvested* — The farmer harvested the wheat at the end of the summer.

- *traditions* — Native American tribes today celebrate many of the traditions of their ancestors.

3. Read Aloud Each Day

Set aside time to read to your child each day. The local library has many nonfiction books about Native Americans, as well as fictional selections. Please refer to the list of books and other resources sent home with the previous family letter, recommending resources related to Native Americans.

4. Using Common Sayings in Everyday Speech

Your child learned the well-known saying "practice makes perfect." The next time your child practices something, you may want to say, "Practice makes perfect!"

Be sure to praise your child whenever s/he shares what has been learned at school.

Name _____

Directions: Cut out the four images that are related to the Lakota Sioux people and tape or glue them on another piece of paper.

Name _____

1. 

2.

3.

4.

5.

6.

7.

8.

9.

10.

Directions: Listen to your teacher's instructions.

11.

12.

13.

14.

15.

Name _____

1.

2.

3.

4.

5.

6.

7.

8.

9.

10.

Directions: Listen to your teacher's instructions.

11.

12.

13.

14.

15.

CORE KNOWLEDGE LANGUAGE ARTS

SERIES EDITOR-IN-CHIEF
E. D. Hirsch, Jr.

PRESIDENT
Linda Bevilacqua

EDITORIAL STAFF
Carolyn Gosse, Senior Editor - Preschool
Khara Turnbull, Materials Development Manager
Michelle L. Warner, Senior Editor - Listening & Learning

Mick Anderson
Robin Blackshire
Maggie Buchanan
Paula Coyner
Sue Fulton
Sara Hunt
Erin Kist
Robin Luecke
Rosie McCormick
Cynthia Peng
Liz Pettit
Ellen Sadler
Deborah Samley
Diane Auger Smith
Sarah Zelinke

DESIGN AND GRAPHICS STAFF
Scott Ritchie, Creative Director

Kim Berrall
Michael Donegan
Liza Greene
Matt Leech
Bridget Moriarty
Lauren Pack

CONSULTING PROJECT MANAGEMENT SERVICES
ScribeConcepts.com

ADDITIONAL CONSULTING SERVICES
Ang Blanchette
Dorrit Green
Carolyn Pinkerton

ACKNOWLEDGMENTS

These materials are the result of the work, advice, and encouragement of numerous individuals over many years. Some of those singled out here already know the depth of our gratitude; others may be surprised to find themselves thanked publicly for help they gave quietly and generously for the sake of the enterprise alone. To helpers named and unnamed we are deeply grateful.

CONTRIBUTORS TO EARLIER VERSIONS OF THESE MATERIALS
Susan B. Albaugh, Kazuko Ashizawa, Nancy Braier, Kathryn M. Cummings, Michelle De Groot, Diana Espinal, Mary E. Forbes, Michael L. Ford, Ted Hirsch, Danielle Knecht, James K. Lee, Diane Henry Leipzig, Martha G. Mack, Liana Mahoney, Isabel McLean, Steve Morrison, Juliane K. Munson, Elizabeth B. Rasmussen, Laura Tortorelli, Rachael L. Shaw, Sivan B. Sherman, Miriam E. Vidaver, Catherine S. Whittington, Jeannette A. Williams

We would like to extend special recognition to Program Directors Matthew Davis and Souzanne Wright who were instrumental to the early development of this program.

SCHOOLS
We are truly grateful to the teachers, students, and administrators of the following schools for their willingness to field test these materials and for their invaluable advice: Capitol View Elementary, Challenge Foundation Academy (IN), Community Academy Public Charter School, Lake Lure Classical Academy, Lepanto Elementary School, New Holland Core Knowledge Academy, Paramount School of Excellence, Pioneer Challenge Foundation Academy, New York City PS 26R (The Carteret School), PS 30X (Wilton School), PS 50X (Clara Barton School), PS 96Q, PS 102X (Joseph O. Loretan), PS 104Q (The Bays Water), PS 214K (Michael Friedsam), PS 223Q (Lyndon B. Johnson School), PS 308K (Clara Cardwell), PS 333Q (Goldie Maple Academy), Sequoyah Elementary School, South Shore Charter Public School, Spartanburg Charter School, Steed Elementary School, Thomas Jefferson Classical Academy, Three Oaks Elementary, West Manor Elementary.

And a special thanks to the CKLA Pilot Coordinators Anita Henderson, Yasmin Lugo-Hernandez, and Susan Smith, whose suggestions and day-to-day support to teachers using these materials in their classrooms was critical.

Core Knowledge®

CREDITS

EXPERT REVIEWER
Jeffrey Hantman

WRITERS
Beth Engel, Rosie McCormick, Cate Whittington, Core Knowledge Staff

ILLUSTRATORS AND IMAGE SOURCES
Take Home Icon: Core Knowledge Staff; 2B-1: Shutterstock; 2B-1 (costumes): Carolyn Wouden; 2B-1 (tepee): Sharae Peterson; 2B-1 (making fire): Apryl Stott; 2B-1 Answer Key: Shutterstock; 2B-1 Answer Key (costume): Carolyn Wouden; 2B-1 Answer Key (tepee): Sharae Peterson; 2B-1 Answer Key (making fire): Apryl Stott; 3B-1: Steve Morrison; PP1: Shutterstock; PP1 (tepee): Sharae Peterson; PP1 (canoe): Library of Congress, Prints and Photographs, LC-USZ62-115473; PP1 (pueblo): Kristin Kwan; PP1 (sewing): Sharae Peterson; PP1 Answer Key: Shutterstock; PP1 Answer Key (tepee): Sharae Peterson; PP1 Answer Key (canoe): Library of Congress, Prints and Photographs, LC-USZ62-115473; PP1 Answer Key (pueblo): Kristin Kwan; PP1 Answer Key (sewing): Sharae Peterson